Young
2004 POETRY

C000089032

ONCE UPON A RHYME

IMAGINATION FOR A NEW GENERATION

Surrey Vol II

Edited by Chris Hallam

 Young**Writers**

First published in Great Britain in 2004 by:
Young Writers
Remus House
Coltsfoot Drive
Peterborough
PE2 9JX
Telephone: 01733 890066
Website: www.youngwriters.co.uk

SB ISBN 1 84460 525 6

Foreword

Young Writers was established in 1991 and has been passionately devoted to the promotion of reading and writing in children and young adults ever since. The quest continues today. Young Writers remains as committed to engendering the fostering of burgeoning poetic and literary talent as ever.

This year's Young Writers competition has proven as vibrant and dynamic as ever and we are delighted to present a showcase of the best poetry from across the UK. Each poem has been carefully selected from a wealth of *Once Upon A Rhyme* entries before ultimately being published in this, our twelfth primary school poetry series.

Once again, we have been supremely impressed by the overall high quality of the entries we have received. The imagination, energy and creativity which has gone into each young writer's entry made choosing the best poems a challenging and often difficult but ultimately hugely rewarding task - the general high standard of the work submitted amply vindicating this opportunity to bring their poetry to a larger appreciative audience.

We sincerely hope you are pleased with our final selection and that you will enjoy *Once Upon A Rhyme Surrey Vol II* for many years to come.

Contents

Christ Church CE Junior School

Harry Jeffery (10)   1
Emma Smith (10)   1
Leah MacKenzie (10)   2
Halle Corrie (10)   2
James Gostage (10)   3
Bonnie Underwood (9)   3
Adam Hitch (10)   4
Chloe Choules (9)   4
Jessica Lawrence (9)   5
Holly Jones (9)   5
Oliver Quinn (10)   6
Jenny Wilkie (9)   6
Laura Tonna-Barthet (9)   7
Sebastian Rocha-Perez (9)   7
Joshua Spellman   8
Evie Hood (11)   8
Stephen Donaghey (11)   9
Prerna Abdaal (10)   9
Millie Witcher (10)   10
Megan Wright (10)   10
Paris Burden (10)   11
Ellis Hudson (11)   11
Sarah Watkins (10)   12
Christopher Hanger (10)   13
Oliver James (10)   13
Jessica Gostage (10)   14
Rebecca Partridge (10)   14
Ben Low (11)   15
Chandni Trehan (10)   15
Katy Lakin (10)   16
Joel Semmens (11)   16
Katrina Cheung (10)   17
Siobhan Webb (10)   18
Andrew Crowe (11)   18
Tom Olorenshaw (11)   19
Anika Choudhury (10)   20

Claygate Primary School

Georgia Dickman (9)	20
Ben Macrae (8)	21
Lucy Freeman (7)	21
Elayda Hearne (9)	22
Edward Hughes (7)	22
Jilly Saunders (8)	23
Nick Ainger (8)	23
Nuri Oglanby (8)	24
Luke Sheavyn (8)	24
Megan Griffiths (8)	25
Helen Edwards (8)	25
Lucy Campbell (8)	26
Alexandra Singer (8)	26
Phoebe Warries (9)	27
Daisy Martin (7)	27
Kate Everett (8)	28
Molly Naylor (8)	28
Alicia Peel (7)	29
Elizabeth Davis (7)	29
Edward Carruthers (9)	30
Paige Murray (9)	30
Lucy Matchett (8)	31
Emma Bentley-Fox (7)	32
Ella Bray (9)	32
Daisy Webb (8)	33
Luke Bentley-Fox (7)	33
Amy Ringshall (7)	34
Holly Skinner (9)	34
Alexandra Panton (7)	35
Anne Hendy (8)	36
Zoe Maycock (8)	36
Stephen Riggs (7)	37
Sian Thomas (7)	37
Kieron Holmes (8)	38
Leah Dixon (8)	38
Georgia Bray (7)	39
Tom Guyatt (9)	40
Eleanor Greening (8)	41
Benjamin Smith (7)	41
Ben Morse (9)	42

Daniel Qureshi (8)   42
Victoria Elkin (7)   43
Lisa Rhodes (9)   44
Adam Pontin (9)   44
Nicholas Nelson (9)   45
Lisa Carruthers (8)   45
Simon Shoebridge (8)   46
Annabel Quick (8)   47
Michael Thomas (9)   47
Saphia Haffejee (8)   48
Lucy Taylor (10)   48
Jake Harris (9)   49
Holly Labacik (8)   49
Kaveh Paymayesh (8)   50
Emilie Myles (9)   50
Jasmine Martin (10)   51
Jamie Latimer (11)   51
Charlie Jerrard (11)   52
Lorna Slessor (9)   52
Max Sisterson (11)   53
Jim Pengilly (9)   53
George Quick (10)   54
Sade MacKinnon (9)   54
Alice Chandler (9)   55
James Edwards (11)   55
Laura Adcock (10)   56
Michael Gostling (10)   56
Jacqui Holmes (10)   57
Hannah Traylen (10)   57
Naomi Everett (10)   58
Taylor Karis (10)   59
Akash Bhanot (11)   59
Beth Cunningham (10)   60
Louise Ainger (10)   60
Leigh Penfold (11)   61
Damien Foreman (9)   61
Lily Gray (10)   62
Sophie Huggins (9)   62
Peter Saunders (11)   63
Jonathan Griffiths (9)   63
Tiffany Pang (9)   64
Charlie Feigen (10)   64

Jack McGrath (10)	65
Hope Cameron-Webb (10)	65
Amy Blake (9)	66

Danetree Junior School

Oliver Lewinski (9)	67
Jordan Tovell (10)	67
Stuart Pitsillides (10)	68
Ryan Woolgar (9)	68
Jack Thorpe (10)	69
Rory Skinner (9)	69
Jeremy Barclay (9)	70
Rabia Baksh (9)	70
Martin Stevenson (9)	71
Hannah Terry (9)	71
Bryony Davies (9)	72
Ashley Burton (10)	72
Sophie White (9)	73
Reiss Newton (8)	73
Olivia Hodgkins (9)	74
Lucy Hill (8)	74
Jack Thompson (9)	75
Emily Post (9)	75
Sophie Field (8)	76
Teige McCarthy (8)	76
Mohammed Hussain (9)	77
Sophie Vincent (9)	77
Rakish Garikedu (10)	78
Alex Banks (8)	78
Laura Gow (9)	79
Peter Gill (10)	79
Scott Henry (10)	80
Matthew Guyett (8)	80
Hannah Everett (10)	81
Holly Dawson (10)	82
Daniel Edwards (9)	82
Mark Keen (9)	83
Charlotte Reid (9)	84
Ellena Revell (10)	85
Katie Bauchop (9)	86
Laura Purdue (9)	86

Caroline Pollard (9)	87
Huw Morgan (9)	87
Laura Gravenell (9)	88
Sagar Patel (8)	88
Paige Bloss (8)	89
Harriet Webb	89
Axel Kemp (11)	90
Lucy Broodbank (10)	91
Alex Webb (9)	91
Samantha Brooks (8)	92
Amy Savage (9)	92
Dominic Worsley (9)	93
Ashleigh McDowell (9)	93
Emma Hamilton (10)	94
George Coates (10)	94
Ellie Chadwick (10)	95
Stevie Syme (10)	95
Madison Pollard (9)	96
Marc Pryor (9)	96
Nathan Stovell (9)	97
Ashleigh Kidd (9)	98
Georga Davies (10)	99
Maisie Grant	99
Leanne Cook (10)	100
Drew Anderson (10)	101
Jamie Workman (8)	101
Nicole Green (10)	102
Hannah Shephard (9)	102
Melissa French (9)	103
Nicole Holloway (9)	103
Lorna Dicken (9)	104
Daniel Underwood (10)	105
Katherine Amer (9)	106
Harry Wales (9)	106
Richard Teare (9)	107
Jamie-Lee Duffell (9)	107
Matthew Halls (9)	108
Levente Green (9)	108
Natasha Inns (9)	109

Downsway School
    Emma Penn (6)   109

Green Wrythe Primary School
    Ashley Jones (11)   110
    Chloe Pearson-Fletcher (10)   110
    Amanda Wessier (10)   111
    Richard Gregory (11)   111
    Joshua Ogenji (11)   112
    Jessica Pryor (10)   112
    Danielle Mulvenna (10)   113
    Emily McDonnell (11)   113
    Jorden Poulton (11)   114
    Tucker Davey (11)   114
    Lauren Powis (11)   115
    Steven Dance (11)   116
    Danielle Staff (10)   116
    Craig Hart (10)   117
    Kyle Duffin (10)   117
    Tyler Chambers (11)   118
    Luke Brown (11)   118
    Carina Lamelas (10)   119
    Antonio Evans Godoy (10)   119
    Jamie Fallows (10)   119
    Daniel Townsend (10)   120
    Adam Barker (11)   120

Northmead Junior School
    Alice Hudson (9)   121
    Catherine Boyton (7)   121
    Sherelyn Norcliffe (9)   122
    Rhiannon Lloyd (8)   122
    Jessica Boyton (9)   123

St Catherine's Preparatory School, Bramley
    Hannah Nicholas (11)   123
    Caitlin Parker (11)   124
    Lizzie Corrie (10)   125
    Ella Davies (11)   126
    Joanna Hitchcock (11)   126

Frances Bird (11)   127
Ellie Buchanan (11)   128
Emily Marmion (10)   129
Zoe Geidelberg (10)   129
Victoria Rea (10)   130
Emma Dane (10)   131
Emma Charatan (10)   132
Helena Muir (10)   133
Philippa Heggie (10)   134
Sophie Johnson (11)   135
Jennifer Salvage (11)   136
Hannah Church (10)   136
Anna Drummond (11)   137
Anna Jordan (11)   138
Sophie Reid (11)   139
Victoria Jefferies (10)   140
Zoe Clarke (11)   140
Catherine Hall (11)   141
Francesca MacVean (11)   141
Maria Pluzhnikov (10)   142
Isabel Healy (10)   142
Sophie Oakes (10)   143
Gaby Custance (10)   143
Alice Facey (10)   144
Hannah Johnson (11)   144
Megan Spalding (10)   145
Katy David (11)   145
Georgina Disney-May (9)   146
Louise Taylor (9)   147
Charlotte Warner (9)   147
Georgina Rolls (10)   148
Megan Burling (10)   148
Isabella Stevens-Harris (9)   149
Elizabeth Dingemans (9)   149
Isabel Bishop (9)   150
Courtney Madincea (10)   150
Abigail Vega (10)   151
Molly Standen-Jewell (10)   152
Emily Wyatt (11)   152
Olivia Frew (10)   153

St Ives School, Haslemere

Lily German (10)	153
Isabella Metcalfe-Smith (10)	154
Alice Steward (9)	154
Georgia Frisby (10)	155
Meredith Leston (10)	155
Christy Callaway-Gale (10)	156
Lydia Matthews (10)	156
Lucy Hawkins (10)	157
Talia Morey (10)	157
Katie Brooke Barnett (10)	158
Charlotte Ashton (9)	158
Lottie Fry (10)	159
Isabella Pettit (10)	159
Lucy Herbert (10)	160
Claire Frye (10)	160
Matya Morey (7)	161
Ellen Hayward (7)	161
Amy Owen (7)	162
Sarah Baldwin (8)	162
Catherine Bird (7)	163
Abigail Hansford (7)	163
Jessica Clifton (8)	164
Rosie Hawkins (8)	164
Lucy Mackintosh (8)	165
Aleena Virdee (7)	165
Alexandra Herson (8)	166
Ellie German (7)	166
Emma Baker (8)	167
Charlotte Taylor (8)	168
Isabella Kirkman (8)	168
Amelia Talfourd-Cook (8)	169
Georgina Gulliver (8)	170
Lauren Evans (7)	170
Ellie Richards (8)	171
Jemima Kuzemko (8)	172
Georgina Wedge (8)	173
Olivia Dower-Tylee (9)	174
Phoebe Smith (8)	175
Lucy Jenner (9)	175
Amelia Frase (8)	176

Eve Franklin (8)   177
Holly Barcham (8)   178
Bobbie Hook (10)   179

St Martin's CE Primary School, Dorking
Lawrence Swithinbank (10)   179
Eleanor Carroll (10)   180
Alexander Jackson (9)   180
Chris Mahony (9)   181
Megan Davey (9)   181
Yasmin Baker (10)   182
Nadia Correa Gomez (9)   182
Hannah Perrin (9)   183
Lucy Holden (9)   183
Rachel Gregson (10)   184
Ben Hardman (9)   184
Dinah Rodell (10)   185
Rosanna Stech (9)   185
Emily O'Brien (10)   185
Zoe Nash (10)   186
Fergus Harding (9)   186
Elsa Hartley (9)   187
Sarah Watson (9)   187
Alex Fyffe (9)   188
Meg Loftus (10)   188
Ben Bessant (9)   188

St Peter's CE (Aided) Primary School, Wrecclesham
Chloe Veale (8)   189
Jonathan Burns (9)   189
Chloe Dibnah (9)   190
Samantha Rogers (8)   190
Martha Teverson (9)   191
Sophie Gale (10)   191
Tom Graham (9)   192
Jonathan Wright (10)   192
Joseph Tindall (9)   193
Shelley MacLachlan (10)   193
Mason Redman (9)   194
Charlie Trenholm (10)   195
Sarah Day (10)   195

Sally Paine (10)	196
Elissa Blankley (10)	196
Charlotte Gregory (10)	197
Jamie Crawford (10)	197
Luke Usher (10)	198
Ryan Gregory (8)	198
Helen Stewart (10)	199
Macauleigh Steel (8)	199
Matthew Bolton (9)	200
Georgia Binfield (7)	200
Susan Wright (10)	201
Erin Beesley (7)	201
Rebecca Cooles (9)	202
Claire Bolton (7)	202
Georgia Cunningham (11)	203
Benjamin Stewart (7)	203
Alastair Viner (11) & Steven Simpson (10)	204
Kirsty MacLachlan (7)	204
Riley Desmond (7)	205
Tommy Marshall (7)	205
Laila Khan (7)	206
Leah Puttick (7)	206
Kirsty Wright (7)	207
Henry Royan (8)	207
Hannah Hillyer (8)	208
Emma Barratt (7)	208

Sandfield CP School

Ghazia Ahmed (10)	209
Jeremy Greenwood (9)	209
Govindi Deerasinghe (9)	210
Tal Parmenter (10)	211
Jake Harris (9)	211
Sarah Millyard (10)	212
Paige Donnithorne (9)	212
Nicole Stracey (9)	213
Vedika Savania (9)	213
Connor Stanton (11)	214
James Colinese (11)	215
Ben Stone (9)	215
Tara Burton (9)	216

Barry Blake (9)	216
Elizabeth Ellis (11)	217
Victoria Howlett (9)	217
Liberty Pollock (10)	218
Christina Drain (11)	218
Natalie Parsons (11)	219
Annabel Holland (9)	219
Alejandra Young (10)	220
Louise Blake (9)	220
Katrien Loots (10)	221
Carolyn Smith (10)	221
Lily Speer (11)	222
Amy Dziwulski (10)	222
Lewis Ellis (10)	223
Reece Killick (11)	223
Hannah Norman (11)	224
Christopher West (11)	224
Yalda Keshavarzi (11)	225

Shottermill Junior School

Eloise Perry (9)	225
David Boxall (9)	226
Alexander Bass (9)	226
Solomon Lawes (8)	227
Nicholas Cherrill (9)	227
Edward Gibson (8)	228
Ben Everitt (8)	228

South Farnham Junior School

Cleo Stringer (10)	229
Holly Hunt (11)	230
Helena Essex (10)	230
Amelia Leishman (11)	231
Polly Rattue (10)	231
Ben Smith (10)	232
Jennifer Keel (10)	233
Jack Miller (11)	234
Jake Duthie (11)	235
George Carroll (10)	236
Alexandra Johnstone (10)	237
Christy Humphreyies (11)	238

Ruby Rowell (10)	239
Robin Humphreyies (11)	240
Rufus Driscoll (11)	241
George Keenan (11)	242
Matthew Parrott (10)	243
Kathryn Burke (10)	244
Jack Deare (10)	245
Helen Schnabel (11)	246
Anneka Butters (10)	247
Charlotte Spratt (10)	248
Sam Hughes (11)	249
Jake Wright (10)	250
Hannah Swannie (11)	251
Melissa Poole (11)	252
Amy Dawson (11)	253
Freddie Wilson (10)	254
Gareth Garland (11)	255
Harriet Foxwell (11)	256
Emily Corrigan (10)	258
Grace Molan (10)	259
Daniel Taylor (10)	260

West Dene School

Maneesha Maini (8)	260
Sona-Kineri Shah (7)	261
Aku-Sheka Allotey (8)	261
Amanda Roper (8)	262
Jackson Rhoden (7)	262
Ayanna Blair-Ford (7)	263
Sydney Davy (7)	263
Sebastian Adeniran-Olule (8)	264
Alice Kerbeck (8)	264

The Poems

My Dad

My dad is clever,
My dad is bright,
My dad is funny,
But he's always starting fights.

My dad loves food,
My dad loves footie,
My dad loves his relatives,
But most of all he loves me.

My dad is always there for me,
All of the day and night.
If I had to choose a dad,
I'd know he'd be just right.

Harry Jeffery (10)
Christ Church CE Junior School

My Brother Daniel

Computer games
Computer games
That's what he always plays
He sits in front of the TV
Nearly every day
He listens to rough music
He never plays with me
But often when he's had his tea
He comes and bothers me.

Emma Smith (10)
Christ Church CE Junior School

My Brother

My brother's a monkey
And very mad as well.
He jumps around all day
And doesn't care what we all say.

He makes the house a mad house
And crawls 'round like a mouse.
But when he goes to school
He looks very cool!
But . . . when he comes back
He looks like he's been crazy.

My brother's a mad monkey.

Leah MacKenzie (10)
Christ Church CE Junior School

My Sister!

My sister chases me around the house
For about ten minutes
She is annoying.
The worst problem is she screams at me.
She tells me to get lost!
She comes into my room
Without asking!
I go into my sister's room
Without asking my sister!
When my sister is kind
She gets on my nerves
Because she acts so sweet!

Halle Corrie (10)
Christ Church CE Junior School

My Cousin Jay

My cousin Jay
Always likes to play
His favourite food to eat
Is different kinds of meat.

My cousin Jay is very sporty
But he is very naughty
He dislikes his mother
And he always hits his brothers.

My cousin Jay
Is rude to his dad
And when he does it
He makes him very mad.

My cousin Jay
Really likes to swim
And because he's nice to me
I'm good friends with him.

James Gostage (10)
Christ Church CE Junior School

My Brother

My brother is a pain in the backside
He gives me dead legs
And he shouts at me so much
He calls me rude words
He tells me to shut up.
I wish he would get lost most of the time.
He and I fight with each other a lot.
He is thirteen
He chases me around the house
I think he is a nerd.

Bonnie Underwood (9)
Christ Church CE Junior School

My Dad

My dad can be very annoying and
sometimes very nice.

But if you get on his bad side when he is
stressed he'll give you a massive
fright.

I love it when it comes to my birthday
because he is always very nice,
and thank goodness never stressed.

He's also very loyal at my football matches.
He hasn't missed one yet and
I hope he never will.

But the best thing about my dad is that
He's always there for me.

Adam Hitch (10)
Christ Church CE Junior School

My Sister Esme

My sister Esme sometimes annoys me,
But sometimes she is kind,
She likes to wear lots of make-up,
And go out with her friends.

My sister Esme takes ages doing her hair,
She is brilliant at horseriding.
Her favourite colour is pink and
I love my sister.

Chloe Choules (9)
Christ Church CE Junior School

My Sister

My sister is a show-off
She thinks she's the best
And acts like a monkey

And is always a pest
And I just want a rest.
My sister is very big
And likes to stroke my
Cat Tig.

She loves to sit in front of the TV
And never wants to play with me.

Jessica Lawrence (9)
Christ Church CE Junior School

My Brother Ross

My brother Ross,
Annoys me all the time.
He is a little monkey,
I hate it when he whines.

My brother Ross,
Plays with me sometimes.
But now he is seven,
So everything is fine.

Holly Jones (9)
Christ Church CE Junior School

My Dad!

My daddy looks like Hitler
With his blonde moustache
He can be quite annoying
And sometimes very harsh.

My daddy can be quite nice
He's just like my lovely mum
But when I am so naughty
He smacks me on the *bum!*

My daddy works away
But sometimes works at home
But every night and day
I talk to him on the phone.

Oliver Quinn (10)
Christ Church CE Junior School

My Sister

My sister is called Tanya,
Her nickname's Tanya Bean.
She can sometimes be quite nice,
And can sometimes be quite mean.

She is mad about her make-up,
And crazy about her hair.
She wears a lot of blusher,
And is picky in what she wears.

She is fifteen years of age,
I think this is very old.
I sometimes call her granny,
As she makes me do as I'm told.

Jenny Wilkie (9)
Christ Church CE Junior School

My Auntie Daphne

My auntie Daphne,
Is quite a funny lady.
She's always laughing or giggling,
Or doing something like that.
My auntie Daphne,
Is always doing something.
Like wrapping a present or cooking dinner,
She never has a break!
She never stops to breathe.
I wonder what keeps her going?
I don't care if she's weird,
I love her so!

Laura Tonna-Barthet (9)
Christ Church CE Junior School

My Dad

My dad is never standing still,
He's got so many jobs.
My dad likes meat but I've never seen him weep.
My dad is strong but he's no King Kong.
He is very funny and he always looks after our pet bunny.
He likes his coffee but he can't eat toffee.
He runs downstairs to get his favourite chair.
My dad is always there for me when I come back home
To have my tea.

Sebastian Rocha-Perez (9)
Christ Church CE Junior School

Matt

There was a young boy called Matt
Who stepped in a cow pat.
He was wearing a welly,
Which became very smelly,
And that was the end of that.

He was walking along,
Singing a song
When just then,
He saw a hen.
He kicked it and it went, splat,
And that was the end of that.

The very next day
He went to play,
He was banging a gong,
Then it went bong,
And that was the end of that.

He fell off a dig
Oh what if,
That was the end of Matt!

Joshua Spellman
Christ Church CE Junior School

Chocolate

Chocolate is my very best friend,
My love for it will never end.
Dark or white, I don't care,
Once I had a chocolate bear.

Chocolate animals, dog or cat,
Someday I'll be very, very fat.
My very favourite is a Dime bar,
Although they're big they don't go far.

Chocolate, chocolate, my love for you,
It's greater than a kangaroo.

Evie Hood (11)
Christ Church CE Junior School

Winter Through My Window

I looked through the window what do I see?
The winter sun blinding me.
The trees look still and straight and motionless
They are silhouetted against the sky,
And in the distance a small plane flying to warmer lands.
The ivy tree is moving with the fluttering of pigeons
As they eat the ivy berries.
Winter is here
The clouds moving westwards, and a solitary seagull flies north
Towards the sea.
Fluffy tails of squirrels leap from tree to tree,
They look like acrobats to me.
Down on the ground leaves lay in piles,
The wind has taken them miles.
The daffodil bulbs spring into life
Under the lonely oak tree.
Soon they will be out for everyone to see,
Winter will be over and spring will be . . .

Stephen Donaghey (11)
Christ Church CE Junior School

Summer

So many butterflies in the air,
Lots of flowers here and there
Cold drinks in the heat,
People dancing to the beat
No more having to stay indoors,
Because everyone's hanging around outdoors
Your brain gets ready to run,
And your parents join in the fun
Summer is a time to have great fun,
That's the same for even a nun.

Prerna Abdaal (10)
Christ Church CE Junior School

The Unknown!

Do you know what will happen tomorrow?
Will it bring happiness, will it bring sorrow?
All of these questions turning round in your head,
Tomorrow, you may even be dead!

You'll never know what the future will hold,
You just fight on and try to be bold.
Whether you will be happy, thoughtful, sad,
Frightened, strong, timid or glad.

All these queries fill you with fear,
What to avoid and what is near.
But don't worry sit back, relax,
Who cares about next week's tax?

Everyone's different perception of life,
Easy going or lots of strife!
I'll let you work it out on your own,
The marvellous or treacherous . . . unknown!

Millie Witcher (10)
Christ Church CE Junior School

All About My Best Friend

I love my best friend.
I can tell her anything, even my deepest, darkest
secrets because I know I can trust her.
I love it when she runs.
I love it when she wags her tail side to side sitting
at my feet looking at me with those deep, dark,
brown eyes and her soppy face when she wants
something.
I love it when she rubs her thick bushy fur
against my face.
I love it when I'm feeling down, she will come up
to me and cheer me up.
If you haven't guessed it by now my best friend
is my dog Kody.

Megan Wright (10)
Christ Church CE Junior School

Flying

Can you imagine if humans could fly?
I'll fly up straight to the sky.
I'll fly up through the clouds,
And look down upon the crowds.

Could you imagine the feeling of not having
your feet on the ground,
But of spinning and falling around and around.

To see birds and planes up in the sky,
And flying with them up high and high.
To go up past the clouds and see the sun,
And feel its warmth while I have some fun.

But now it's time to come back down and put
my feet back on the ground,
Because after all, even though I can fly,
I do not have a bed in the sky.

Paris Burden (10)
Christ Church CE Junior School

Squashed

Whack! Nearly hit me.
Whack! Hit it back.
Whack! Hold the racket.
Whack! Get in the corner.
Whack! Hit it hard.
Whack! Racket up.
Whack! That was close.
Whack! Get to the back.
Whack! Perfect hit.
Phew! Glad that's over!

Ellis Hudson (11)
Christ Church CE Junior School

My Rabbit

My rabbit loves carrots,
But hates parrots.
He loves to dig
And gets muddy
Just like a pig.
He's cute and cuddly
With a white fluffy tail.

My rabbit loves to munch
He's good at lunch.
He lies in daisies
Which make him smell
And he likes being lazy.
He is eight years old
And his birthday is in March.

My rabbit loves me,
But hates bees.
He's very cheeky,
And he's a bit naughty.
But most of all sneaky.
He's chocolate and white
And he's called Jim!

Sarah Watkins (10)
Christ Church CE Junior School

Bad Weather

As an earthquake rips through the ground
Houses clinging to the hillside.
A stream running down is drained into the ground
People jumping here and there.
Everyone's had quite a scare.
Cars rolling round and round
As an earthquake rips through the ground.

As a hurricane tears through a town,
Earth and rubble chucked around.
Lots of fright, lots of sound,
As a hurricane tears through a town.

As an avalanche roars down, down
Lots of people trying to escape its jaws.
As an avalanche roars down, down.

Christopher Hanger (10)
Christ Church CE Junior School

My New Football Boots

On Friday when in the shops
I saw some football boots, 50% off.

I bought them and wore them to training,
I played quite well but didn't care, it's only training.

On Sunday I wore them at a match
And started playing really well.

Half-time had already come and I'd already scored three goals.
Then the second half came and we were already attacking.

After all that work my boots scored six,
My new boots are great, I really like my boots.

Oliver James (10)
Christ Church CE Junior School

A Poem About My Family And Me!

My name is Jessica Gostage I am ten years old.

My brother went to Portugal to collect a pot of gold
And on the way he caught a cough
And an extremely nasty cold.

My sister went to Ireland to sail the seven seas
Then she went to the park and was stung by a swarm of bees.

My mum went to the seaside to go and have some fun
And then she went to the baker's to buy a gigantic sticky bun.

My dad went to watch football, his team tried hard to score,
He was jumping up and down so much he fell right through
the floor.

I hope you enjoyed my poem, I think it's time to go,
An early start tomorrow, it's school I'll have you know.

Jessica Gostage (10)
Christ Church CE Junior School

Horses

Horses tall, ponies small,
Black ones, white ones,
I like them all.

See them grazing in the sun,
Stallions, mares and foals,
Trotting round having fun.

See them in the field so green,
Enjoying the sweet juicy grass.
Just been groomed, all shiny and clean.

Baby foals bouncing round with excitement
Stallions stand tall watching over them all,
Of course along with Mum.

Rebecca Partridge (10)
Christ Church CE Junior School

Andre Agassi

Andre Agassi, my favourite tennis player in the world
With his perfect serve that is always curled
And his lightning dash
That goes well with his smash!

His beautiful forehand and backhand strokes
Keep his opponents busy with no time for jokes,
And his skilful spins
That go well with his wins!

His amazing accurate angles
Always keeps his opponents in tangles,
And his trickful dropshot
Makes his opponents lose the lot!

His terrific topspin lob
Makes his opponents sob,
And his fantastic play altogether
Cannot be disturbed by any weather!

Ben Low (11)
Christ Church CE Junior School

A Winter's Day

As I sit here, watching the rain, feeling so low,
I cannot wait for the moment when it will snow.

We all sit here, crowded comfortably around the fire,
Sipping hot cocoa and crouched on an old car tyre.

Everyone looks at each other with a sad look,
We've got nothing to do, except from reading an adventure
book.

Oh how I wish I could be in the story I read,
Far away from this misery as I am freed.

But back to reality, I am stuck here with poverty and pain,
No one to listen to me except for these silent drops of rain.

Chandni Trehan (10)
Christ Church CE Junior School

My Dog

My dog used to run
But now he's old he just sits in the sun
He relaxes and thinks
What shall I have to drink?
I know, some beer
Or red wine because water is boring
He puts his hand on his head
And says
I know, some lemonade will do
Then he gets his pyjamas on
And starts singing himself to sleep!
He doesn't know if he is a dog or a man
My dog has the best collar
It says 'Am I a dog or man?'
Whenever somebody walks past
He ducks down and pretends he's asleep.

Katy Lakin (10)
Christ Church CE Junior School

The UFO

It was ten o'clock at Disneyland
And I was standing on a stand,
When I looked up and I saw,
A sight so full of wonder, galore!

A UFO hovered there,
Yes there, in the air!
So shiny orange, (and a bit blurry)
But it wasn't at all furry!

It stalled a bit,
While I sit,
Then shot away
To meet me another day!

Joel Semmens (11)
Christ Church CE Junior School

My Monster

I have a monster that lives under my bed
He has curly hair, which is yellow and red.
'It's nice to meet you dear fellow,' he said.
Then he struggled to get back under my bed.

On his big, fluffy, purple head he sat,
With a *thump!* Right on my blue bumpy mat.
He flew around with his wings like a bat
And his five tails flapped about like a cat.

He has a spiky, grey, scaly back.
Which on he hangs his golden lunchpack.
Also he hangs on a large black sack
Which in he puts a big holey pink mac.

He popped out to see me the very next day,
I think he only had one thing to say.
'I seem to always come and pass your way
But I'll be leaving the very next day.'

I ruffled his curly, red, fluffy hair
Then he gave me a hug, just like a bear.
As he went, I wished him the best of care,
Then off he trotted on his pretty little mare.

Katrina Cheung (10)
Christ Church CE Junior School

My Brother Nick

My brother Nick,
Doesn't miss a trick.
When we watch TV
He always has to pick!

My brother Nick,
You shouldn't mess with him
I'm not joking,
He'll throw you in the bin.

My brother Nick,
Is six foot four
When we watch his programmes,
We all end up in a bore!

Well my brother Nick
Is *sometimes* nice to me
Well he's my brother
He has to be!

Siobhan Webb (10)
Christ Church CE Junior School

Animals

Snakes sliding slithering slyly
Mice munching moving mischievously
Rabbits running rustling restlessly
Dogs drooling digging deeply
Cats crawling creeping cautiously
Ducks dawdling diving delicately
Goats grazing grass graciously
Worms wriggling watching whatever
Swans swimming swooping silently
Rats roaming running roughly
Spiders scuttling spying skilfully.

Andrew Crowe (11)
Christ Church CE Junior School

Seasons

S ummer is a nice warm time.
U nder the trees you rest.
M aybe invite your friends to play.
M aybe get your paddling pool out.
E veryone goes to the park to play.
R eason for this, it's summer!

W inter only comes to freeze the Earth.
I n the snow children play.
N ever wanting the snow to go away.
T rees get covered in snow and shiver.
E veryone having snow fights.
R eason for this, it's winter!

A utumn is the colour time.
U nder the trees the leaves drop.
T rees turn bare, looking embarrassed.
U nder the trees the colours arrive.
M aybe people like this for the colours.
N o one is at home, they go for a walk.

S pring comes for cleaning.
P eople clean their houses.
R eason for this, everyone spring cleans.
I n spring blossom appears on the trees.
N ew buds everywhere bursting with colour.
G oing to the park, people stare at the pink trees.

Tom Olorenshaw (11)
Christ Church CE Junior School

Seasons

The flowers start to grow,
The sun starts to come out,
As the breeze gently blows,
As the children run about.

The sun gives out its beams,
We are all playing in the park,
As we all taste the lovely ice creams,
As the dogs start to bark.

The leaves gently fall,
The sun starts to disappear,
Everyone starts to put away their balls,
As the sky starts to clear.

The snow is here,
As the Christmas festivals begin,
We all cheer,
As we all regain.

Anika Choudhury (10)
Christ Church CE Junior School

Snow Melting

One day when I went to school,
There was lots of snow on the icy pool,
But then came out Mrs James
Who spoilt it all in just a few flames.
'You silly, silly children why come out today?'
'But Mrs James! The sun will have melted all the snow away.
We're bored inside, with wet play games,
Here with Mrs Haines,
We'd rather be outside,
Playing on our new slide.'

Georgia Dickman (9)
Claygate Primary School

Three Little Pigs

T here once were three little pigs.
H ow small their house was and how little space they had.
'R ight,' they said, 'We need to find our own places to live.'
E ach of the pigs set off down the road to find themselves a house.
E asily, the first little pig built a house of straw.

L ater, the second little pig quickly built a house of sticks
'I am going to build a house of bricks,' said the third, clever pig.
T o the first little pig's surprise there was a knock at the door.
It was the big bad wolf!
T he big bad wolf said, 'I will huff and I'll puff and I'll blow your
house down.'
L onging for safety the two pigs ran to their brother's house.
E xhausted the pigs lay down but the wolf soon caught up and
came calling there too.

'P erhaps I shall climb down the chimney,' growled the wolf.
I mmediately the pigs popped a pot of boiling water in the
fireplace.
G reedily the wolf climbed down the chimney and fell into the pot.
He shot back up and was never seen again!
S afe and sound the three little pigs lived together happily
ever after.

Ben Macrae (8)
Claygate Primary School

Yum-Yum

Dip, flip, snip, whip,
I smell the blood of a giant chip.
Be he fat or be he small,
I'll cook him crunchy and I will eat him all.

Lucy Freeman (7)
Claygate Primary School

Cold Tea

When you get home
On a cold winter's day
Drop your bag and throw your homework away.
Make your mum happy
And give her some tea.
(You might get some extra pocket money).
Boil the kettle with cold water in
Get a mug and put the warm water in.
Put a teabag inside the mug
And stir it with a spoon.
Not forgetting take the teabag out
Then put sugar or milk in (Mum likes sugar best).
Now it would be a bit hot
Leave it by the window sill.
Then go and watch *Lord of the Rings!*
And when it is finished
Collect the tea and take it up to your mum
But take a tray in case . . . whoops
I've made it cold.

Elayda Hearne (9)
Claygate Primary School

The Monster

Fig, fag, fog, fug,
I smell the blood of a giant bug.
Be he light or be he dark,
I'll cut him in half to make my ark!

Edward Hughes (7)
Claygate Primary School

Making A Cup Of Tea

To make your mum happy
It won't make her sad
Give her a cup of tea
And a biscuit that's chocolatey.
Put on the kettle
Get out a cup,
Tell your mum to settle
Make your dad cheer her up,
Get a tea bag
Put it in the pot,
Mum don't you nag
It'll be nice and hot,
Pour in the water
And give it a stir,
About a quarter (of water)
Then give it to her.

Jilly Saunders (8)
Claygate Primary School

How Snow Melts

The sun comes down from a blue blanket and
lights up white crystals glittering on the ground.
The crystals turn into water and spread like a
pond waving round a tree.
Water separates like steam glistening on the ground
Like crystals in the sea.
Sucked up into the trees
That's where the water goes.

Nick Ainger (8)
Claygate Primary School

The Berries

The day in the woods
I picked some berries
Then a bear ate them all
I picked some more.
Then I accidentally boiled them all
And then I squished them all inside the pie.
The bear came again to eat me up
So I gave him the pie and he ate it all up.
I had to give it to him
Or he would have gobbled me up!

Nuri Oglanby (8)
Claygate Primary School

Winning A Football Match

All the players came out on the pitch
We won the toss without a hitch
Started play and scored a goal
And all the players lost their souls
All their fans shouted at the ref
One of them said, 'He must be deaf.'
Our keeper made a good catch
And we went on to win the match.

Luke Sheavyn (8)
Claygate Primary School

How To Make A Cup Of Tea

If your mum wants a cup of tea and she's feeling ill,
You can make it for her, it will make her feel brill.
First you boil some water in the kettle,
Get a cup and pour the hot water out.
Put a tea bag in the cup,
'Can I remind you there's lots of running about.'
Take the teabag out of the cup,
Take a tray out of the drawer,
Put the cup of tea on the tray.
'Oops, I spilt a bit, don't spill anymore!'
Get some sugar and a jug of milk,
Stir it up until it's smooth as silk.
Take it to your mum
And it will make her say, 'Yum-yum!'

Megan Griffiths (8)
Claygate Primary School

The Day I Made A Weird Cake

I can show you how to make a very, very weird cake.
Just get some pepper, just pour it right in.
Because today my mum's ill and she's given me a chill.

Egg, ham, chips and the rest
Will fill my mum's tum
Out of her vest.

Then I bring the cake
And my mum gets mad
'What a bad girl making a cake with all of my jam.'

Then she tried it and what a surprise
She thought it was horrib-lovely as a bride!

Helen Edwards (8)
Claygate Primary School

Potion Lesson

Firstly we will learn how to make eyeball banana skins,
So we know who falls for the old tricks.
Collect a child and take out their eyes
Next grab and take a banana skin.
Go down to the dungeon and put them both in the cauldron
Add a bit of leftovers and pour them in.
Go outside and collect some weeds
Take them down and pour them in.
Give it a stir or two,
Oh don't forget a bit of hair
And a feather from a chair.
Also a toad.
Put in the toad
Give it five stirs
Pull out the banana skin
Lay it on the floor outside
And see who falls for it.

Lucy Campbell (8)
Claygate Primary School

Life Cycle Of A Butterfly

Butterflies are pretty flying in the sky,
A rainbow of colours flapping in my garden.

First a butterfly lays eggs on a leaf
When the eggs hatch it's a caterpillar.
They're like wriggly worms but green instead.
'Whatever I find I shall eat,' said the little caterpillar.
So first he found an apple, ice cream
Then he thought, *I think a leaf might be better.*

Alexandra Singer (8)
Claygate Primary School

A Dog's Life

Week 1
A puppy starts off the size of a mouse,
It could even get lost in a big fat house.
So get it a box that it can't get out,
The box can be small because a pup's only stout.
It closes its eyes but can smell very well
It can hear from a whisper to the sound of a bell.

Week 2
The cute little pup can now open its eyes.
Now it walks instead of lies.
Now it can see it explores lots of things
It chews up old loo paper and rips up old slings.

One year
The pup is now big and strong like a bull
Now its food bowl isn't half full.
Well don't you think that I'm a believer,
But that pup is now a golden retriever!

Phoebe Warries (9)
Claygate Primary School

When Does It Go?

The snow came down just last night
It's very cold and very bright.
It hasn't gone for quite a long time
The first time I saw it, it hit my eyes
And then I rushed right out to play,
Then I shouted, *'Hip, hip, hooray!'*
I called my friends out to play
They brought their sledges and their sleigh.
It got cold, we went inside
The sun came out the very next day
With such bad luck the snow went away.

Daisy Martin (7)
Claygate Primary School

How To Make A Cup Of Tea

I'm making a cup of tea for me
But how do I do it?
I'll see what I can do
I know I'll pour it through.

How to make a cup of tea.
It's very hard, you see.
I boil the kettle,
And then it's done.
I pour in a cup
But it's not brown!
So I pour some mud into it.
Umm Yum-yum!
Yuck!
It's horrible.
I don't like tea.
Yeah he!

Kate Everett (8)
Claygate Primary School

Making A Zoo

To make a zoo is a hullabaloo
And this is how you do it.
You get a gate
And lay it straight
And get some cages
That pay such wages.
But that's not all the hullabaloo
Get some animals in a hat
But you mustn't forget the cat, oh of course
And the fat rat
And there you have a zoo
But remember it's a hullabaloo.

Molly Naylor (8)
Claygate Primary School

How To Make A Cup Of Tea

I wake up early one morning
And look at my chart
Oh no! Today it's my mum's birthday.
I say I will make her a cup of tea.
With no help, just only me.
Put hot water in the kettle
And put it on
Get out a cup
Put it on the side next to the kettle
When it has finished boiling
Put a teabag in
Fish it out with a spoon
And put it in the bin.
Get some milk from the fridge
And put it in your cup
Mix it with the spoon,
You need to get the teabag out.

Alicia Peel (7)
Claygate Primary School

How To Make Hot Chocolate

On a cold winter's night I opened the cupboard
And saw a lovely big jar of hot chocolate.
First of all you boil the kettle,
Get the cup and spoon the chocolate in it.
Then add the hot water and whisk it
Next add the milk so that it makes it cooler.
In order to make it frothy,
You must whisk it immediately.
Hot chocolate is so creamy every sip is another treat,
And I have it as often as I can.
It warms me up from head to toe.

Elizabeth Davis (7)
Claygate Primary School

Sorry

I am very sorry that
I broke your trophy Dad.
I am so sorry that I fed
Your hamster the wrong food Sophie.
I am very sorry that I let the cat scratch your chair,
And had a pillow fight with my friend Mum.
I am very, very, very sorry that I shaved off your hair
And used your radio as a robot friend Dad.
I cannot believe that I walked the dog into a wall
Sorry dog.
Next thing I knew
I ran down the loo, my mum found a stain on the canary
Sorry canary and Mum.
What is the world coming to?
Do you know?
I don't.

Edward Carruthers (9)
Claygate Primary School

Dear Dad

While you were in Amsterdam I was so bored
So I played with the birds
And they pecked your car sixteen times.

I was reading 'Tracy Beaker'
And a witch came through the door
And tore that invention called Robolina.

You know those blue curtains you got?
The cat tied them in a great big knot.

Sorry I was very bad
The cat got a flea and went super duper mad.

Paige Murray (9)
Claygate Primary School

How To Tell A Little Lie

Dear Dad

I am sure the house was not very tidy
Even if it was last Friday.
When I came home from school
A fingerprint appeared on the wall.
A very small splash of tea
Emerged on the priceless painting of me
That only cost one hundred pounds
I am sorry to say it fell to the ground.

As well as that
I am sorry old chap
Your wallet has disappeared
And your credit card bills have gone up high.
You better pay them before you die.

I am sorry about the fish Dad
There's no need to have a fit lad.
When I was cleaning them out (oo)
They sort of, er, fell down the loo.

Oh by the way how is Mum?
I can't talk now I'm on the run.

So thank you for taking the time
To read this carefully written rhyme.

Lucy Matchett (8)
Claygate Primary School

How To Fly A Paper Plane

One day I sat and felt so bored,
So up I got.
Can you guess, I made a paper plane.
Lesson One
Put it in your hand and let it go,
Oh dear.
Lesson two,
Put it in your hand and push it and let it go,
Miaow, miaow! Oops!
Make it stop with your hands, ouch!
Lesson three
Stand in the way to stop it,
Oh no, duck.
Lesson four
Don't try this at home kids.

Emma Bentley-Fox (7)
Claygate Primary School

Snow Melting

Snow falls on the ground
Like leaves in the autumn breeze
Then children come from all around
They play on it and it turns to ice.
Then it gets too slippery
And all the children go away
What a way to end the day
Then the sun comes out
Like a steaming hot tomato on a cold winter's day
Then the sun breaks the ice
Like crackling eggs in a pan
It gradually melts away
Like an iceberg floating away.

Ella Bray (9)
Claygate Primary School

The Three Billy Goats Gruff

The three Billy goats wanted to eat nicer grass
But the big mean troll wouldn't let them pass
The first little goat said, 'I am only small
I would not fill you up at all.'
The troll decided to let him go through.

The second goat said, 'I am only little too
I would not make much of a snack for you.'
The troll decided to let him go through.

The third goat said, 'I'm as big and tough as you.'
And with one big hoof he kicked the troll to Timbuktu.
The goat decided to go through.

Daisy Webb (8)
Claygate Primary School

Little Red Riding Hood

There once was a girl called Red Riding Hood
Who went for a walk in a faraway wood,
But while she was there,
She saw a big bear,
So they had a bun fight in the mud.

Luke Bentley-Fox (7)
Claygate Primary School

How To Make A Cup Of Tea

One day I crept downstairs
It was my mum's birthday.
I want to make her happy
So I switched on the kettle
It did not work.
Oh yes it needs cold water
Then I poured it in a bowl.
Oh no you need a mug
But Mum said not to touch those
They're my precious mugs.
So I got a plastic cup oh - well that's fine
I poured the water in the cup
That's not the right colour so I put some chocolate in.
Then I tasted it
Yuck! I hate cups of tea.

Amy Ringshall (7)
Claygate Primary School

Cinderella

Cinderella was in the cellar
Imagining her prince would call.
Her fairy appeared to come to tell her that
She would go to the ball.

She longed to meet a prince to marry
So she could travel in a big gold carriage.
In the end she went to the ball
She met the prince and they did fall . . .
In love.

Holly Skinner (9)
Claygate Primary School

Snow White

Snow White is sad, her mum has died
Oh good! She's got a new mum.
Her secret is her magic mirror
It hangs on the wall without a shimmer.
She is the prettiest, oh no, oh no,
She is to be killed by a knight.
'Run into the wood,' he says kindly.
She runs, she trips, she's hurt.
She manages to make it to a house.
She goes inside and finds a mouse.
The dwarves come home
They find Snow White
She tells them her story
They are very kind
They say she can stay.
She does the housework every day.
The queen is furious
Then she makes a plan
She kills Snow White by poisoning an apple.
A prince comes along and wakes her up with a kiss
She goes off with the prince
She is very happy
She says goodbye
The queen has died.
'Yippee hooray,' she says with laughter
And she lives happily ever after.

Alexandra Panton (7)
Claygate Primary School

Snow White And The Seven Dwarves

Snow White went into the woods
She tripped on a root and her tears were like floods.
She stumbled to a cottage
And found small bowls of pottage.
'Who could live here?' she wondered.

She went upstairs to have a rest
And put on a big white vest
The beds were so small
And she was so tall
But she managed to have a sleep.

Then in came seven dwarves so bright
And gave Snow White a terrible fright.
They made a deal
To keep the house clean
But one dwarf was so mean.

They let her stay
Snow White was glad because she did not have to pay.
She gave Grumpy a wash
With a splish and a splosh
And made herself at home.

Anne Hendy (8)
Claygate Primary School

Snow White And The Seven Dwarves

Once upon a time lived a princess called Snow White.
She often cleaned under the dazzling light.
She had skin as white as snow.
Her lips royal red and did glow.
She was upset for her love was not yet there.
She was taken to a house by a nice big bear.
She loved the little house
In that house there was a mouse
The rooms were dusty
The pots were crusty.

Zoe Maycock (8)
Claygate Primary School

The Three Little Pigs

The first pig built his house with straw
But the wolf came along and banged on the door.

And said, 'I'll huff and I'll puff and I'll blow
Your house down,' and did.

The second pig built his house with sticks
But the wolf came along and played his tricks.

And said, 'I'll huff and I'll puff and I'll blow
Your house down,' and did.

The third pig built his house with bricks
But the wolf came along and played his tricks.

And said, 'I'll huff and I'll puff and I'll blow
Your house down,' but could not.

So he came down the chimney and landed on the fire
Just what he deserved, the naughty liar.

Stephen Riggs (7)
Claygate Primary School

Cinderella

C inderella down the cellar cleaning as she does
I t's dusty, it's rusty, she hates it like her sisters.
N aughty and snorty, just like their mother
D ressed they are in frilly dresses going to a ball
E very girl wanted to meet the prince that night
R eally the sisters gave him a fright
E ven the coachmen thought they were ugly
L ots of people thought Cinderella was lovely
L ove came to the prince and Cinderella
A fter the ball he came to fetch her.

Sian Thomas (7)
Claygate Primary School

The Three Little Pigs

The first little pig built his house with sticks
He thought to himself, *these will do the trick.*
Even the wolf shouted, 'I'll huff and I'll puff and I'll blow
your house down,' with his big guff.

The second little pig built his house with sand
He thought to himself, *this is just like land.*
Remember, 'I'll huff and I'll puff and I'll blow your house down,'
bellowed the wolf with his big guff.
Even the third little pig built his house with bricks.
Even he knows bricks will do the trick.
'I'll huff and I'll puff and I'll blow your house down,' shouted
the wolf.
'Problem,' he whispered.
He went down the chimney but the fire was on and he burnt
his bum!
'I'll have a celebration!' cried the pig.
'Great news everyone the wolf is dead!' shouted the pig.
'Super celebrations! Come on,' replied the pig.
The End.

Kieron Holmes (8)
Claygate Primary School

Snow White

Young Snow White such a beautiful sight.
Ate a bad apple
Gave the dwarves a fright
Her mother gave a sparkling light.

Leah Dixon (8)
Claygate Primary School

Silly Jack And The Beanstalk

There was a boy who was very silly
And his name was Jack.
He sold a cow and bought some beans
From an old man's shop.

When he got back from the market
His mother was mad
She said, 'Jack, why did you do that?'
And threw away the beans.

In the night the beans grew and grew
Until they made a beanstalk
Jack thought he would climb it while
His mother was fast asleep.

He climbed and climbed to the top of the stalk
At the top there was a castle
With a giant and golden hen
That wouldn't lay golden eggs.

Jack stole the hen when it laid an egg
But he couldn't carry it.
The giant looked around and found Jack
And started to chase him.

Jack got away and climbed back down the stalk
The giant was behind him.
Jack called his mum to get an axe
And cut the stalk down dead.

Jack kept his hen which laid golden eggs
Which made him very rich.
He gave beans to everyone around the town
And lived a happy life.

Georgia Bray (7)
Claygate Primary School

Goldilocks And The Three Bears

G oldilocks walking down the street
'O h good,' she saw the house under the tree
L ooking inside
D elicious-looking porridge pie
'I hate this, yuck,' she said as she ate the first bowl
L ucky enough the second one was almost OK.
O n to the last bowl
'C ome on,' said Goldilocks. 'This should be the best.'
K eenly she finished it up and feeling full
S he wanted to sit down

A nd she tried the first chair, 'This is much too big.'
N ow she tried the second chair, 'This is much too soft.'
'D ear me!' cried Goldilocks when she broke the last chair.

T hen Goldilocks crept up the stairs
'H ey!' said Goldilocks when she saw the beds
E ager to sleep in a bed.

'T oo uncomfortable,' said Goldilocks to the first one
H urried to the second -
'R ubbish!' she exclaimed as she tried it out
E ventually, Goldilocks said, 'This is the one for me.'
E very other bear that lived in that house came in.

B aby Bear came in first, followed by Mummy and Daddy Bear
E very time they went into a room things had changed.
A s Baby said, 'What's going on? Mine's all wrong,'
R unning down the stairs, Goldilocks shouted, 'Where've you been?
   I couldn't wait!'
'S ister Bear why did you eat my tea and break my chair?
   It's not fair!'

Tom Guyatt (9)
Claygate Primary School

Sleeping Beauty

There once was a girl called Sleeping Beauty
She really was such a cutie.
There also was a mean old witch
Who tried to play horrible tricks.
She cast a spell over the beauty
That on her 18th birthday she would prick her finger and fall asleep.
Then ever so quick time flew, it was her 18th birthday
She found a strange thing with which to play
She pricked her finger and faded away.
Then a handsome prince came
His horse had become lame
But the witch had grown a forest round the castle
It looked like a great big prickly parcel.
He chopped it down with a great big sword
He was so busy he didn't get bored.
He kissed the princess who woke up with a smile
They got married and danced up the aisle.

Eleanor Greening (8)
Claygate Primary School

The Three Billy Goats Gruff

The littlest Billy Goat Gruff crossed the bridge one day
And found a troll to his dismay
He thought of his horns
Which were the size of thorns
Which were no use to him at all.

But he bravely said, 'Please don't eat me
I'm only very skinny and also very small'
And then the troll did notice that
It was very true and after that
He went back under
And with a little smile on his face
He trotted over the bridge and nibbled at the grass.

Benjamin Smith (7)
Claygate Primary School

Making A Cup Of Tea

One day when you're old
and you're very cold,
you might need a cup of tea,
and this is how you make it.
Pour some cold water in the kettle and let it boil.
When it has boiled pour it into a mug
and drop a tea bag in it.
And if you miss it try again.
When you've finally got it in, stir it,
put the milk and the sugar and stir (if you like it!)
When you've finished
put it on a tray
and put the tray into your mum's arms.

Ben Morse (9)
Claygate Primary School

Cinderella

Cinderella lived in a cellar
She had to clean lots of dishes and pots
Her step-sisters picked on her lots
Then she heard the doorbell ring
So she went to the door
And there was a letter on the floor.
It said the prince was having an eighteenth
Birthday party
Cinderella was shocked and started karate.
She went upstairs
But her wardrobe was bare
And that was the sad end to that!

Daniel Qureshi (8)
Claygate Primary School

Little Red Riding Hood

Little Red Riding Hood ran through the woods to see her
old grandma but then she saw a dinosaur!
I don't know why but she clapped and cheered for the dinosaur.
The girl went on and on into the dark woods
The time had passed and Little Red Riding Hood stopped to
eat an apple.
'Ekk!' she cried, the dinosaur tried to hide. 'Hi, I mean goodbye!'
Dark shadows it looked like a witch's shadow.
Little Red Riding Hood screamed and ran and ran for her life!
In the dark house Grandma was lying in bed
Dark lights above her then she saw the dinosaur
In he went. He locked Grandma in the cupboard
'No, no!' she screamed.
'Grandma stay there.'
'Good morning Grandma, not meaning to be rude
But you have grown a lot. You've got sharp teeth.'
'Have I?'
'Yes a lot.'
'Help, help!'
'Who's that?'
'Me, Grandma.'
'Oh darling Red Riding Hood, where have you been?'
'Oh look Grandma the dinosaur has gone.'
Dark little cottage is now safe and sound
But who knows what will happen tomorrow.

Victoria Elkin (7)
Claygate Primary School

Goldilocks Came Into The House

Yum! Yum! Goldilocks spotted a bowl of steaming hot
porridge.
'Help! Help!' said a little mouse.
The bears came back from their daily saunter
To find a girl had wandered into their pleasant little shack.
Goldilocks took flight with much haste
Upon the sight of the three bears appearing in their
little shack.
The bears shook their heads as they looked on in shock
Staying warm within their shack each winter night
Hoping one day the golden child would visit them once again.

Lisa Rhodes (9)
Claygate Primary School

The Three Little Pigs

The first little pig built his house from straw
Then the wolf came knocking on his door
But the pig just said, 'Go away
And don't come back here anymore.'
The second little pig built his house of sticks
And then the wolf came running with some tricks.
And then he huffed and puffed as he licked his lips.
The third little pig made his house of bricks
And the wolf came running and gave it a kick.
He jumped up and down and cried and cried
And leapt down the chimney and nearly died.

Adam Pontin (9)
Claygate Primary School

The Three Little Pigs

The three little pigs go marching quickly to find a house.
Here comes the big bad wolf run for your life *argh.*
'Right quickly get into your house,' said one of the pigs.
Eeek the big bad wolf is going to blow down the grass house.
'Every pig run for your life,' said the biggest pig.
'Let's lock the door before the wolf gets in and gobbles us up,' said
one of the pigs.
'I want to eat all of you pigs at once,' said the big bad wolf.
The first little pig is building his house out of grass.
'Try and blow my house down,' squealed the pig.
'Look here comes the big bad wolf,' said one of the pigs.
Every little pig built a different house.
Pity the first little pig didn't know where the second pig was.
'I'll huff and I'll puff until I blow your house down,' said the wolf.
'Go to the brick house,' said the second pig.
'See houses made of bricks are best,' said the third pig.

Nicholas Nelson (9)
Claygate Primary School

Planting A Rose

To make your garden look lovely
Plant in a rose or two!
Take the rose twist it out, mind your nose!
Dig a hole, dig it well!
Put the rose into the hole
And pack it round with soil.
Take a can and fill it up
Water the rose till it reaches your toes!
Leave it out there in the sunshine
Keep it there and it'll be fine!
That's how you make your garden look lovely
By planting in a rose or two!

Lisa Carruthers (8)
Claygate Primary School

Goldilocks

As I was walking through the wood
In a sunny clearing stood
A lovely cottage coloured pink
Which made me stop to think.

Who lived in such a pretty house
Perhaps it was a little mouse
As I opened up the door
What was that I saw?

Three steaming bowls of oats
Could it be a house for goats?
Perhaps I could have a little bite
Too hot, too cold, then just right.

Maybe it's all that fresh air
I'm so tired I need a chair
Too hard, too soft, then just right
Will it break, I think it might!

Up the stairs to bed I go
Hope I find a comfy throw
Too hard, too soft, then just right
I think I'll settle for the night.

While waiting for their oats to cool
Three bears went to visit the pool
On their return to great dismay
They found someone had come to stay.

An empty bowl and broken chair
Was that some silky golden hair?
Up the stairs to have a peep
A little girl they found asleep.

A roar, a scream,
Was it all a nasty dream?
I jumped and ran down the stair
All they could see was my flying hair.

Simon Shoebridge (8)
Claygate Primary School

Cinderella

Cinderella was a maid,
in a house where she didn't get paid.

Near a palace she sits alone waiting for
the prince to phone.

Day in day out she scrubs the floors.

Even the windows and the doors.

Ring, ring, ring the doorbell went with an
invitation to her sent.

Eventually she found some clothes to wear
to their night out.

Looking like a million pounds she arrives at
his palace.

Loving what she has seen so far she can't
wait to get twice as far.

And finally they fall in love and get married
and have a baby called Alice.

Annabel Quick (8)
Claygate Primary School

Snowfall

People make snowmen with friends.
The unique qualities of snow
Makes families smile with joy.

Snowballs thrown at teachers
The sound is crunchy, the feeling is wet,
The snow reflects the light.

Now the snow is going!
We better use it up
But now the snow is gone.

Michael Thomas (9)
Claygate Primary School

Making The World

The world is an interesting thing to make
It's as easy as baking a cake.
You don't need to hurry
You don't need to scurry
Just be a creator and make!
Grab a ball of Blue-tack
Give it a roll and a smack!
But when it is rolled
It will look rather bald.
So add a colour or two!
Build on a castle,
As big as a parcel and say:
'I'm the creator of the
World!'
But if your mum does not approve
Consider her she's rather rude!
But the thing that is the best is
You get to have a rest!

Saphia Haffejee (8)
Claygate Primary School

Snow

Like a soft pillowed blanket
It lays on the ground
It looks like some white glitter
Crunching on the grass.
All the leaves twinkle in snow
Twigs fall to the mud
Everyone makes white snowmen
At the end of the day
No one shouts 'Hooray!'
We all go to bed
And wait for the next cold day.

Lucy Taylor (10)
Claygate Primary School

Waiting For The Baby

When you find out
That your mum's gonna have a baby
You normally get really excited.
Sometimes it's very good if you can go
to her next scan.
'Of course.'
So off you go.
When you are there you could ask her doctor
What it's gonna be.
It's very annoying that the baby won't come quickly.
Because you don't really know what it's gonna be.
But when the time comes for it to come
You get more excited than ever.
When it's born however
It seems magical
That Mum's created life on Earth.

Jake Harris (9)
Claygate Primary School

Cinderella

C inderella in the cellar
I n her rags so torn
N asty sisters wish she'd never been born
D usting and cleaning all day long
E very day a chore to be done
R eally she would love to dance at the palace
E veryone would love to dance with the prince
L ots of joy when a fairy godmother appeared
L ove flew around her head dancing with the prince
A lways living happily ever after.

Holly Labacik (8)
Claygate Primary School

The Three Little Pigs

T here was once three little pigs
H owever they wanted to move house
E very day they wished they could move.

T he days went on and they had to go
H owever, they did not go in the forest!
'R ight,' said the little pig, 'I will make my house of straw.'
E veryone said, 'Make your house of straw but don't let Mr Wolf roar.'
E veryone was missing the little pig.

L ittle pig built a house of straw and he didn't know it was
                                                against the law.
I n the meanwhile when the little pig was in his house,
                                          Mr Wolf arrived.
T ap, tap, 'I don't have a trap,' said the wolf.
T he pig would not let Mr Wolf in.
L ittle pig was scared.
'E h,' said the pig. 'Should I dig out of my house?'

'P oor little pig,' said the wolf, 'I will eat you!
I 'll huff and puff and blow the house down!'
'G uff!' went the wolf and blew the house down.
'S orry,' went the pig and ran for his life.

Kaveh Paymayesh (8)
Claygate Primary School

The Falling Snow

The snow is falling
The icicles are hanging on
Cold is the feeling.

The crunchy feeling
The snow looks like falling glitter
A blanket of snow.

The snow has fallen
Glistening, shimmering snow
Reflecting the sun.

Emilie Myles (9)
Claygate Primary School

A Winter's Day

I stood on the outside white soft blanket,
I looked around for an adventure to begin.
The icy air blew right through me,
As I walked on, the cold bit at my skin.
I carried on walking as far as I could,
I watched and I listened to everything there.
A wonderful view hit my eyes,
The roaring wind swallowed me up.
I wished for fire right by my side.
The last snowdrop fell,
The last we shall see,
Till next winter so that should be.
As I went home all I took were memories,
And left nothing but footprints,
On a winter's day.

Jasmine Martin (10)
Claygate Primary School

Winter

The icy cold air biting at my toes
As the snow comes flooding down.
The ice-cold snow pierced my heart
And the pain ran through my body.
As I walked through the icy depths
Of the cold wind
Crawling my way through the white blanket.
Icy knives stabbed my fingers
Each drop pierced my skin
Sending a chill wind down my back.
As I crushed through the snow
Icicles caught in my shoes.
As it fell from the sky
Like a howling wind of wolves
It covers our land in snow.

Jamie Latimer (11)
Claygate Primary School

Harold Bone

Carelessness and family free
Harold Bone drove carelessly!
Whilst on the phone
He broke every bone.
He was a fine old chap
He didn't own a map.
Harold crashed into a wall
He had a major fall.
There was blood and guts and even more
Everything fell off, even the door.
The car went up in flames
He heard loads of names.
There was a short moan
It was Harold Bone.
The poor old chap was *dead!*
His mother and pa were still in bed.
The funeral was arranged the very next day
It was a very sad day, in May,
And there Harold Bone lay.

Charlie Jerrard (11)
Claygate Primary School

A Snowy Scene

Like a sheep's woolly jumper
And icing sugar falling.
Under your feet it sounds crunchy
The wind sounds like it's calling.

Layers of snow on the trees
Like scoops of ice cream
The field's whole whiteness
Is like a snowy dream.

Footprints in the snow
Like pictures on the floor
There's not much snow left
I hope we'll get some more!

Lorna Slessor (9)
Claygate Primary School

The Snowfall At Dayfall

The snow is like a
Blanket of cotton wool
Keeping the grass warm.

Icicles are
Hanging off the branches
Like sharp knives.

A snowman
Stands by himself
In the field.

Snowballs fly
Through the air
Like white doves.

Max Sisterson (11)
Claygate Primary School

Winter Snow

Winter snow shining bright,
Enough for a snowball fight,
Winter snow brown and white
Enough for a mud ball fight.

Kids coming out to play,
On this very special day,
Shouting hip hip hooray,
On this very special day.

When they're out they will shout,
'Come and play, oh come and play.'
Winter snow shining bright,
Never ever go away.

Jim Pengilly (9)
Claygate Primary School

Harold Bone

Harold Bone was a carefree chap,
In his car reading a map,
Carelessness and fancy free,
Harold Bone drove carelessly,
Driving in his red toned car,
Telephoning from afar,
The policeman saw him on the phone,
Naughty, naughty Harold Bone.
Suddenly a chase broke out,
Driving round the roundabout,
Quick they chased him to and fro,
Everywhere he would go,
Without a care who he hit,
Harold Bone was a careless twit.
Blood, guts and gore everywhere it went,
And all the car was left with was a little dent.

George Quick (10)
Claygate Primary School

Snake Slithers

I saw a snake that slithers everywhere
I went to the fair to see a bear
The snake is pink and green
Where has the snake been?

Sade MacKinnon (9)
Claygate Primary School

My Ice Palace

I walk outside into the cold, bitter night air
I slip on my wellies
I am an ice queen, tall and proud
The snow-covered playground is my ice palace
Under the climbing frame is a ballroom
The whirling snowflakes are dancers
Their elegant clothes are torn by the chill wind
Between the swings are the guest rooms
Filled with snow-white blankets laid neatly in rows
Inside the tree house sit rats eating away at the
white feast
An owl hoots to the fox
'Come and play, come and play'
The icy turrets and snowy chambers
Belong to an ice palace
My ice palace!

Alice Chandler (9)
Claygate Primary School

Snow

It fell from the sky to cover my world
as it had covered its own.
It howls like a wolf under the moon
when it is alone.
It fell from the sky, the moon, the stars
as it did years ago.
This is the thing which changed our world
the thing we call snow.

James Edwards (11)
Claygate Primary School

How To Write A Poem

H ear me, watch me, copy me now
O nly if you want to I'll show you how
W ith all the lines and metaphors too.

T his thing is definitely made for you
O n the subject pick up a pencil and pen

W ith this help you'll be able to write more than ten
R hyming is a cheerful thing
 I t's like learning to ride, jump and sing
T hough you do not have to do it
E verything like this will help you through it

A nd in the end, you know it's true.

P erfect poems come from me and you
O nly when you listen to me
E verybody will now see
M aking poems comes naturally.

Laura Adcock (10)
Claygate Primary School

My Snow Poem

The white, cold curtain fell from the sky
To make my world white
The icy air took my breath
Just like it did my friends'
All I could do was stop and stare
Stare at my whitening world
Just to think
Think of what the white world would be
Like in the morning.

Michael Gostling (10)
Claygate Primary School

A Winter's Day

The cold air bites at me,
The cold air turns about
The wind blows at me,
The wind gives a shout,
A shout of thick air,
Brushes right past me,
A shout of thick air,
Goes right through me,
These are the things on a winter's day,
So wrap up warm and keep that way.

The cold air swallows me up,
The cold air bites at my skin,
I then pick up my burning hot cup
Full of a fire
I am just glad I had a good day
I'm wrapped up warm and kept that way!

Jacqui Holmes (10)
Claygate Primary School

Arctic Snow Bears

I looked out of my bedroom window
I was in the warm and in the dry
I thought of the bears
Far away in the Arctic.
In the deep snow and tall pine trees
That is their home,
They like it there,
They're happy there,
I felt their cold, wet, frosty noses,
I blew the snow from their strong, bold backs,
I stroked their brown backs,
As if they were the Arctic bears I longed to hold.

Hannah Traylen (10)
Claygate Primary School

The Ice Wizard

Inside and warm,
Watching the storm,
Go to bed,
Wake up rise your head,
Then go outside,
I slip and slide,
Then from nowhere,
It hit my hair,
I fell to the ground,
All spiky not round,
It stabbed me I was caught,
The terror it had bought,
I rose and ran really fast,
But the thing it had a blast,
Soon there started a blizzard,
I could tell it was the ice wizard,
He bit me right to my veins
I could feel so much pain,
My mum had told me I barely listened,
It only happened when the ice glistened,
I soon recovered from such terror and fright,
I opened my eyes and saw the light,
I ran and ran until I was home,
But how, but how he was less than a bone,
The winter went by and the summer soon came,
My mum kept telling me again and again,
I went outside it was like a sun blizzard,
But then I saw it was the sun wizard.

Naomi Everett (10)
Claygate Primary School

Winter Splinter

Winter Splinter giving us pain,
Nibbling us all over,
Winter Splinter ruining our game,
There's us slipping over,
Winter Splinter making us lame,
Freezing our legs,
Winter Splinter covering the land,
Like an icy white blanket.
Winter Splinter going away,
Thinking he's lost a game,
We all shout, *'Hooray!'*

Taylor Karis (10)
Claygate Primary School

Cold

I look out my snow-layered window
And see a street in Moscow or Tokyo
I thought it was a major hoax
But then I saw our snow-ridden cloaks
The icy cold snow falling from the sky
Just to pop in and say 'Hi'
Then comes the blizzard of snow, so cold
It comes and grabs my lungs
Going everywhere on the ladder rungs
Now it's going
Like a lawnmower mowing.

Akash Bhanot (11)
Claygate Primary School

Walking In The Snow!

Crunching snow under my feet
Keeping to the beat
Making footprints in the snow
Not knowing where to go.

Hiding under the ground
Crumbling not to be found
Footprints everywhere
It's only ever fair.

It's like hiding under a blanket
The snow has almost sank it
Scrunching up the snow
It's like ripping paper.

Muddy footprints ruining it
When you hold it, it crumbles to bits
Hold it in your bare hands,
Your teeth make a chattering, like a rock band.

Everybody play in the snow
No one will ever say no!

Beth Cunningham (10)
Claygate Primary School

Snowfall

Icy white creamy snow blizzards
falling to the ground.

Glitter twirling to the ground
sparkling but cannot be found.

Icing sugar with glitter soft as can be
you can see it in the trees.

Sounds like crunched up biscuits
but crumbles in your hands
and gets caught in the leaves.

Louise Ainger (10)
Claygate Primary School

Winter Graveyard

The seasons of the Earth
Give birth.
When the clock turns to winter, it is time to die,
For I do not tell a lie.

In the depths of the winter chill,
The winter broken creatures are ill.
My eyes feel them,
My heart is heavy, pounding again and again.

Is this it?
As the hammer made of ice and rage starts to hit.
It's a maze of craze,
A runaway for freedom.

There is only one way
This is the day.
The new generation . . .
Will fear the new isolation.

Leigh Penfold (11)
Claygate Primary School

Snow Feelings Haiku

Crunchy snow, sparkling,
In all the patterns fab white,
Happy snow feeling.

Damien Foreman (9)
Claygate Primary School

The Snow Soul

The snow soul that lies beneath,
Jack Frost is a thief, he steals,
Catching your breath and warmth too.
Crispy softness under your feet,
The snow is a servant for Jack Frost.
They are stealing your heat.

It is cold outside, I hide,
Snow is cold, very cold
It's so cold I want to hide.

The sun is a yellow balloon
Floating up high in the blue,
blue sky.
Rising up in red, yellow and pink.

The snow is going away,
It was fun to play with,
Let's wait for another day!

Lily Gray (10)
Claygate Primary School

Example Of A Murderer

J umped out on people
A larmed ladies
C heeky
K iller

T ossed
H istorical
E xecuted ladies

R ed blood all over him
I n the night it is dangerous
P olicemen can't catch him
P elvis ripped open
E xample of a murderer
R ipper rageous.

Sophie Huggins (9)
Claygate Primary School

The Snowman

I stood and stared at the snow gently falling down and laying
itself upon the subtle ground,
Trying to draw back the fluffy white curtains,
I looked again into the gloomy night,
My heart ticked slower than a broken clock,
When I saw this terrible sight,
There he stood,
With his hawthorn arms swaying in the howling wind,
Snow fell from his body like crumbs from a biscuit,
The Leaning Tower of Pisa frozen solid to his head,
A part of Hell whirled around my body,
As I watched the raging gale decapitate the snowman.

Peter Saunders (11)
Claygate Primary School

Killer Spider

Uncle Paul sitting on the wall,
Eating a cottage pie,
Along came a spider with his poisonous fangs,
And said, 'I absolutely lie.'
So the spider came down onto the throne,
And broke in his leg a bone.

Jonathan Griffiths (9)
Claygate Primary School

My Family

My mum has fabulous dresses
And hates horrible messes.
She will tidy them up very fast
Then Mum will have some tea at last!

My dad is a businessman
He has many friends named Chan
He is a loyal friend and a lovely dad
And that isn't because he doesn't get mad!

I have three sisters, one, two and three
So they're on my family tree
I am the youngest, the baby too
So they're the old ones that already grew!

We have a lot of pets of different heights
Two rabbits, one cat, a Persian type.
One dog named Muchi that's who
Also two tortoises too!

So that's my family they are a big one
And they're all really fun
I have a lovely family all of them together
They'll be in my heart for now and forever!

Tiffany Pang (9)
Claygate Primary School

Goliath Tall

There once was a man who was nine feet tall
And his name was Goliath, he was an enemy of Saul.
He killed and he killed the Philistines
And a thought hit Saul's mind.
That new king maybe he will fight
But then Saul fought and had a fright.

Charlie Feigen (10)
Claygate Primary School

Blood Snow

As the icy blood covers the ground
Nails, fingers hanging down
The ice covers my feet like snakes
And the air bites me like a howling dog
As darkness covers the starless sky
Spikes drop from the sky onto me
The footprints disappear under the spikes and blood
As I am getting tense an owl hoots
I fall to the ground I get straight up
A nail scratches me across the face, I clench
Thunder fills the sky
I hear my mum calling as I make a break for it
I get home my mum asks me what happened
I say, 'Nothing.'

Jack McGrath (10)
Claygate Primary School

The Spirit Of Snow

The flakes are like feathers falling through the sky,
The snow is like fluffy white cushions on a bed,
The sky is like a baby-blue blanket over the snow.

The icicles dangling on the trees are like glasses of milk
on a bedside table,
The snow is resting peacefully like a little girl sleeping silently.

The trees are covered in snow like a cake smothered
in cream.

The last flake has fallen,
We watch as the spirit of the snow fades away,
As day slides into night.

Hope Cameron-Webb (10)
Claygate Primary School

On A Mountain

On a mountain,
You'll never find a fountain.
It's sometimes 2000 feet tall
I thought I was going to fall.
Is that a bear
Over there
Or is it a yak?
I'm starting to crack.
I think I'm going back!

You'll never get up in a day,
It's not the place you want to play,
Careful you don't lose your way.
You'll need to take a tent,
Don't worry about any rent.

I feel so proud
I'm out of the clouds.
I'm back on the ground,
It's flat all around.
My adventure is over,
I'm back with my dog Rover.

Amy Blake (9)
Claygate Primary School

The Mouse

Small and brown he lives in the ground
He likes to run around and around,
With a long pink tail
And teeth like a nail,
His claws are like knives
He's got lots of wives!

His whiskers are white
Watch out he might bite,
He likes to scurry
He's always in a hurry
His name is Scouse
And he is a mouse.

Oliver Lewinski (9)
Danetree Junior School

James Bond 007

James Bond is like a black bomb,
He carries a warther P99,
It's always loaded with at least one bullet,
One shot will kill the villain.
You see him in a black suit,
If you're not careful the shot might be for you.
He drinks a vodka martini,
He drives an Aston Martin.
He's always looking for trouble
He never fails a mission
And goes by the name 007.

Jordan Tovell (10)
Danetree Junior School

Penguins Slide

Happily across the Antarctic
Penguins may slide
Maybe into the water
They will decide.

Penguins diving in and out
Without any doubt.
Having lots of fun
Till the day is done.

Night has now fallen
The penguins settle down
Fast asleep they are falling
Until there's not a sound.

Stuart Pitsillides (10)
Danetree Junior School

Terry Eames Is Magic

Terry Eames is magic
He wears a magic hat and
When we started AFC
He said, 'I'm having that'
He swears when average
He swears when rubbish
And when we win the CCL
He'll swear all night.

Ryan Woolgar (9)
Danetree Junior School

Monkey Playground

In the monkey playground
Even all around
There are slides and swings
You can hear monkeys sing
'Go inside' the teacher would say
Let's go inside it's the end of the day.
The monkeys sigh
And say goodbye
They don't want to go
By the time they leave
It will be Christmas Eve
When they get home
They might moan
Their mum will pick them up on the highway
Better luck tomorrow
Then they all realise it's Friday
But one cheeky monkey asked if he could have
Three barbecues
And a pair of shoes.

Jack Thorpe (10)
Danetree Junior School

James Bond

He is as strong as thunder
He is as fast as a tornado
He is as agile as a cheetah
He is as fit as a dog
He is as energetic as a Ferrari motor
He is as intelligent as a dolphin
He is as cunning as a fox
He is as slick as a cat.

Rory Skinner (9)
Danetree Junior School

Untitled

I'm a popular kid - it has to be said, said, said
And all the other kids want to be dead, dead, dead!
I mock them, tease them - make them cry
They all think why, why, why?

For I am a great bully-ee
'Mercy, mercy' the victims plea.
But the mummies and the daddies never find out
Because, 'If you tell, I'll get you!' I always shout.

But sooner or later I got degraded
All my fame and power faded
Now I'm unpopular - yes it's true
For the initiation test - I didn't get through.

I'm not a popular kid - it has to be said, said, said.
Now I want to be dead, dead, dead!
They mock me, tease me - make me cry,
Now I think, *why, why, why?*

Jeremy Barclay (9)
Danetree Junior School

There Is A Dragon Inside me

There is a mean dragon inside me
That makes me pull my sister's hair.
There is a silly dragon inside me
That breaks everything down.
There is a funny dragon inside me
That makes me laugh.
There is a quiet dragon inside me
When no sound comes out.
There is a noisy dragon inside me
That makes me scream out loud.

Rabia Baksh (9)
Danetree Junior School

Noises In The Jungle

Cheetahs running
Bees humming
Zebras eating
Lions meeting
By the tree.
Kangaroos jumping
Elephants bumping
Antelopes drinking
Hippos singing
By the tree.
Rhinos stamping
Hunters camping
Monkeys swinging
Birds singing
By the tree.

Martin Stevenson (9)
Danetree Junior School

The Dragons Inside Me

There is a shy dragon inside me that makes no words come out.
There is a mean dragon inside me that makes me shout,
There is a naughty dragon inside me that makes me steal,
There is a greedy dragon inside me that makes me eat every meal,
There is a brave dragon inside me that makes me say, 'That's mine.'
There is a nervous dragon inside me
That sends shivers down my spine.

Hannah Terry (9)
Danetree Junior School

Noises In The Jungle

Tigers growling, lions prowling,
Zebras drinking
By the water hole.

Snakes hissing, tarantulas crawling,
Antelope drinking
By the water hole.

Elephants stamping, parrots squawking,
Deer drinking
By the water hole.

Hyenas laughing, hippos bathing,
Monkeys drinking
By the water hole.

Mice running, crocodiles hiding,
Hunters drinking
By the water hole.

Bryony Davies (9)
Danetree Junior School

Where's Everyone?

In the cloakroom wet coats hanging up
In the office dinner money piled in pounds
In the head's room half a cup of hot tea
In the corridor cupboards but no crowds
In the hall wooden floors apparatus
In the classrooms unread books and unsharpened pencils.
In the meantime in the playground . . .
A fire drill.

Ashley Burton (10)
Danetree Junior School

The Dragons Inside Me

There's a funny dragon inside me
That makes me want to laugh
There's a noisy dragon inside me
That makes me want to scream
There's a naughty dragon inside me
That makes me want to pinch
There's a quiet dragon inside me
That seems I've lost my voice
There's a helpful dragon inside me
That makes me want to clean up
There's a silly dragon inside me
That makes me want to get drunk
There's a fierce dragon inside me
That makes me want to roar
There's a nervous dragon inside me
That makes me quite scared
Of dragons!

Sophie White (9)
Danetree Junior School

Untitled

There is a bad dragon inside me that makes me steal.
There is a mean dragon inside me that makes me slam doors.
There is a robber dragon inside me that makes me rob banks.
There is a friendly dragon inside me that makes me play football.
There is a clever dragon inside me that makes me get full marks.

Reiss Newton (8)
Danetree Junior School

Disneyland

We are going to go to a fab place,
Which happens to be called Disney
I'm so excited I can't wait
To meet all the characters
And stay up very (very) late!

The big rides are exciting
They go so very fast,
As I look over the sides,
The trees go whizzing past.

Pirates of the Caribbean,
Peter Pan and Dumbo too,
These are just a few of the rides,
But there's loads more to do.

Leaving is the sad bit,
We've really had great fun
Disney is such a special place
It's *my* holiday number one.

Olivia Hodgkins (9)
Danetree Junior School

The Playground

In the playground boys are shouting, *'goal!'*
Girls are skipping around, people shouting and cheering.
Being nosy and getting into other people's business.
Children looking curious.
Teachers drinking tea and eating lots of chocolate.
Children getting sent to the wall
To stand alone.
We go to lunch and then back to class
And be as quiet as can be.

Lucy Hill (8)
Danetree Junior School

Noises In The Marching Band

In the marching band there are . . .
Drums booming,
Trumpets trumping,
Xylophones tinging.

In the marching band there are . . .
Whistles blowing,
Violins whining beautifully
Tin drums binging.

In the marching band there are . . .
Pianos dinging,
Cymbals crashing,
Flutes whistling.

I love to follow the marching band.

Jack Thompson (9)
Danetree Junior School

The Playground

Children screaming,
Has a meaning,
It means someone's hurt,
The teacher runs over,
Really quickly to Rover,
The little boy that's hurt,
He's hurt his knee.
'Who was it?'
'Not me.'
Said a little boy.
'Well he broke my toy,'
Said a boy called Roy.
'You must not annoy.'
Said the teacher to Roy,
'Toys are here to enjoy.'

Emily Post (9)
Danetree Junior School

The Dragon Inside Me

There is a worried dragon inside me wondering
if she's going to tell on me.
There is a nosy dragon inside me wondering
if she's talking about me.
There is a nervous dragon inside me wondering
if I should go through with this.
There is a mean dragon inside me that makes
me *shout*.
There is a helpful dragon inside me that
wants to clean the house.
There is a playful dragon inside me that wants to
play with Roy and his toys.

    So if the dragon does this to me
        where will I be . . .?

Sophie Field (8)
Danetree Junior School

The Dragons Inside Me

There's a naughty dragon inside me
That makes me pull my sister's hair.
There's a helpful dragon inside me
That makes me tidy my bedroom.
There's a funny dragon inside me
That makes me want to laugh.
There's a silly dragon inside me
That makes me want to get drunk.
There's a brave dragon inside me
That makes me go mountain climbing.
There's a quiet dragon inside me
That makes me lose my voice.

Teige McCarthy (8)
Danetree Junior School

Noises In The Jungle

Noises in the jungle everywhere
Tigers are roaring,
Frogs are jumping,
Noises in the jungle everywhere!

Bees are buzzing,
Monkeys are swinging,
Lions are pouncing.

Noises in the jungle everywhere.
Rhinos are charging
Elephants are stamping
Snakes are hissing.

Noises in the jungle everywhere
Zebras are drinking
Lizards are running
Cheetahs are blasting forward
Noises in the jungle everywhere!

Mohammed Hussain (9)
Danetree Junior School

Bad Dream

Every night I get a fright
Then I saw a flying kite
The next day I got a bite
The next day I saw a knight
Having a dreadful fight.
When I woke it was bright
I saw a bright light
When I saw the bite
I screamed.

Sophie Vincent (9)
Danetree Junior School

Joy To The World

Joy to the world
The pigs are dead
We barbecued their heads,
We flushed their bodies down the toilet,
We flushed their bodies down the toilet
And round and round it went and round and round it went
And round and round it went!

Joy to the world the alien's dead,
We barbecued his head,
We flushed his body down the toilet,
We flushed his body down the toilet,
And round and round it went and round and round it went
And round and round it went!

Rakish Garikedu (10)
Danetree Junior School

There Is A Dragon Inside Me

There is a brave dragon inside me,
That makes me want to go to the front of the line
At the dentist.
There is a mean dragon inside me
That makes me pull my sister's hair.
There is a quiet dragon inside me
When I'm reading books.
There is a silly dragon inside me
That makes me laugh all the time.
There is a naughty dragon inside me
That makes me shout at my mum.
There is a helpful dragon inside me
That cleans my brain!

Alex Banks (8)
Danetree Junior School

Paris

It was at Easter time
That I went to Paris.
I went with my family
Because we were invited
To celebrate my grandad's birthday.

We went on a bus
And then on a train.
We arrived at the park
And unpacked our bags.
We went on some rides,
We went up and down
We saw Mickey Mouse
And all of his friends.

Laura Gow (9)
Danetree Junior School

Curse Of The Super Trike

There was a young schoolboy called Mike,
Who went everywhere on his trike,
The wheels were all blue,
And no longer new,
What he really wanted was a new bike.

The same young schoolboy called Mike,
On his birthday list he only wrote 'Bike',
His birthday it came,
He got a PlayStation game,
'The Curse of the Super Trike'.

Peter Gill (10)
Danetree Junior School

My Grandparents' Holiday

On 2nd December 2003
My nanna Jo and Grandy
Left their house at 3 o'clock
To make their way to the docks.

They took their car and caravan
And off they went to find a tan.
They drove down to Spain
To get away from the British rain.

They found a site
Which was alright.
There they are by the caravan
Laying down with a good suntan.

On Christmas Eve they could not wait
So they ended up staying up late.
On Christmas Day they went to church
And met a girl called Laura Birch.

They rang me to tell me
They had not been swimming in the sea
On February 29th 2004
They caught a boat to British shores.

Scott Henry (10)
Danetree Junior School

The Playground

In the playground there's children playing football
scoring loads of goals.
In the playground there's children playing rugby,
passing balls backwards.
In the playground children attending the talent contest.
In the playground children singing, dancing.
Children getting told off for climbing fences by the headmaster.
Bad.

Matthew Guyett (8)
Danetree Junior School

My Family

My uncle David likes to eat,
Especially ice cream as well as his meat.
My auntie Jo is as potty as can be,
I suppose that some of that rubs off in me!
My sister Rachel is in Year 8,
I think she's really great!
My auntie Penny is as small as a mouse,
But she lives in a very big house.
My uncle Henry is very funny
And he does have a lot of money.
My cousin Lauren loves horses,
She rides them over different courses.
Then there's Amy with my cousin John,
In New Zealand they shouldn't be long.
Also there is Chris and Phil
We stayed with them once, it was brill.
My cousin Hayley is very tall,
But my cousin Bethany is quite small.
My mum Catherine is very kind,
Someone like her is hard to find.
My granny lives far away,
I really enjoy it when we go to stay.
My dad has a large family tree,
The best thing is, they're all related to me!

Hannah Everett (10)
Danetree Junior School

Holidays

My heavenly holiday
I like to build sandcastles
as big as you and me,
or to build tiny ones that get washed into the sea.

My nose can smell that fruity
Juicy suntan cream
And the strawberry twirls of a
soft ice cream.

It's scary climbing in the dark
gloomy caves but it's really good fun
to go splashing in the waves.

I love to watch the sunset
as it gently fades away
and then get excited
about another day.

Holly Dawson (10)
Danetree Junior School

My Best Friends

Peter is my best friend
I've known him since I was four
I think he is rather clever
I wished he lived next door.

Jeremy is my best friend
I think he is funny
He always makes me laugh and smile
And he rather likes honey.

Elliot is my best friend
His favourite sport is football.
He makes a great goalkeeper
Even though he is quite small.

Daniel Edwards (9)
Danetree Junior School

Untitled

On Saturday I went out on my bike to the park
Every time I rang my bell it made the dogs bark
I rode really fast on the path
And fell off in a puddle and needed a bath.
I had to walk home all muddy and wet.

When I got home and had a hot bath
Me and Mum sat down and had a good laugh.
We talked about what happened in the park
We laughed and laughed until it was dark.

At 10 o'clock I went up to bed
And pulled the quilt up to my head.
I snuggled up all cosy and warm
And watched the moon and stars till dawn.

Woke up late on Sunday morning
To the smell of breakfast calling
The day was all sunny and bright
I shielded my eyes from the light.

My nan and grandad came over for dinner
Mum cooked lamb with honey and ginger.
We ate until we could eat no more
Then Nan and Grandad headed for the door.

Mark Keen (9)
Danetree Junior School

Seasons

W inter's here
I t's cold outside
N ights are long and dark
T he snow is falling
E veryone's calling
R un and have fun in the park.

S pring is here, it's back so soon
P retty flowers are in bloom
R oses and primroses are all about
I t will be summer soon
N ights are shorter, days are sunny
G o and find the Easter bunny!

S ummer is back
U nable to keep cool
M ust go for a swim in the swimming pool.
M aking sandcastles
E ating ice cream, paddling in
R ock pools, rivers and streams.

A utumn's here, it's back again
U mbrellas are blowing away.
T alking children rake the leaves
U nable to stand up on a windy day.
M asks are made for Hallowe'en
N ow it's time to shout and scream!

Charlotte Reid (9)
Danetree Junior School

Seasons

In the depths of winter
When a white blanket is on the ground
And lots of little robins are hopping all around
It's in the depths of winter
People trudge through the snow
Huddled in thick warm coats as the frosty wind begins to blow
And then the season begins to change as winter turns to spring.
When all the frost has cleared away
And all the seagulls fly around the bay.
Little lambs jump and leap
And flowers appear by our feet.
Then the seasons change again as spring turns to summer
When the trees are green and the sun is hot
This is the season I like a lot.
I will splash and play by the pool all day
And when sun hides away
I go slowly off to bed
And cuddle close to me, my ted.
Slowly the seasons change again as summer turns to autumn
Juicy fruit is on the trees.
I walk through leaves up to my knees
Flocks of birds fly southward bound
My feet squelch on the soft ground.
Slowly but surely the days get colder,
As the winter again taps the land on its shoulder.

Ellena Revell (10)
Danetree Junior School

Spring, Summer, Autumn, Winter

Flowers growing, buds are new
Daisies, daffodils, tulips too.
Baby lambs are being born,
Smells of freshly mown lawn.

People sitting in the sun
Sand and water is such fun
Beaches full of shells and stones
Children licking ice cream cones.

Leaves falling off the trees
All blowing in the breeze
Red, orange, yellow, brown
A mass of colour falling down.

Children having snowball fights
Just before the long dark nights
Christmas now drawing near
The end of another year.

Katie Bauchop (9)
Danetree Junior School

When I Go To Florida

When I go to Florida I'm going on a plane
The long hours are a pain
I'm staying in a villa with a pool
It's very cool.
On the plane we chat
The pool is fat.
We're going very far
So we'll have to hire a car.
We're going to see the rockets
With some money in our pockets.
We are going for two weeks
I want to see some ducks with beaks.
We're not going until Easter 2005
So by then I will have learnt to drive.

Laura Purdue (9)
Danetree Junior School

Playgrounds

Playing at break it's so fun
Especially when you play in the sun.
If I had a chocolate bun
I wouldn't even leave a crumb
I don't like to hear children cry
Because they don't get their favourite pie.

You can run very fast
I wish I wasn't always last.
I swing on the chin up bars
I always want to drive a car.

I love playing football on the field
The other team had to yield.
Some people have skipping races,
Make sure you don't trip over your laces.

Caroline Pollard (9)
Danetree Junior School

On Holiday

When I am on holiday I play on the beach
When I am on holiday I play on the beach
and it is within my reach.
When I am on holiday I play on the beach
and I make a sandcastle.
When I am on holiday I play on the beach
and wrap my brothers in a sand parcel.

When I am on holiday I stay in my villa and I sleep on my pillow.
When I am on holiday I stay in my villa and I sleep under the willow
When I am on holiday I stay in my villa, I have a swim and I
go to the gym.

Huw Morgan (9)
Danetree Junior School

My Brother

When I got home from school today
My brother wanted to go out to play.
But I could not go out today,
And I didn't want to play in the hay.

He moaned and groaned and whinged and whined,
He pestered and pestered till I blew my mind.
'OK, OK, I'll play today,
I'll play with you outside in the hay!

But promise me this, my little brother
If I don't tell our dear old mother,
You'll help me do my homework!'
('Cause he's really quite smart!)

Laura Gravenell (9)
Danetree Junior School

The Playground

Boys playing football
Girls playing hopscotch
Teachers are drinking their tea
Boys are playing with me
Girls are going to lunch
Boys are going munch, munch, munch.

Sagar Patel (8)
Danetree Junior School

There's A Dragon Inside Me

There's a brave dragon inside me
That makes me want to line up first at the hospital.

There's a noisy dragon inside me
That makes me want to shout.

There's a mean dragon inside me
That makes me want to pull my brother's hair.

There's a nice dragon inside me
That makes me want to help alot.

There's a funny dragon inside me
That makes me want to smile.

There's a silly dragon inside me
That makes me want to put my shoes on the wrong feet.

Paige Bloss (8)
Danetree Junior School

The Sky

I look at the sun and ask my mum
'Will today be fun?'
Mum looks at the sun, she smiles and grins,
And says 'I think the park! Oh yes will be fun for me.'
I look at the stars in the sky so bright they never fight.
They shine so bright.
I look at the moon so white and bright
He comes out at night,
The moon is as high as a kite.

Harriet Webb
Danetree Junior School

When The Fighters

When the mercenary uses his sword in fight
The enemy would freeze in fright
And when he stabs with utter glee
The enemy would shout 'Spare me!'

When the brigand swings his axe in battle
His allies bear a fearful rattle
As the blade pierces through the air
And leaves the enemy in deep despair.

When the archer fires his bolts in skirmish
It makes all units feel quite squirmish
When it is time to break the moor
There is a small 'thud' and they fall to the floor.

When the myrmidon thrusts his sword in combat
With gauntlets made from skin of bat
And when the enemy wishes they were better led.
A flail of the rapier and they are dead.

When the berserker wields his oars in melee
The enemy would shout 'Parley!'
And if the enemy has the upper hand one day
He has the ability to sail away.

When the fighters learn to forever slay
The enemies think that they should pay
For compensation that they dealt first
With lots of revenge, their bubble would burst.

Together, this forms fighters, a band
They always lend a helping hand
The axe wielders, sword and crossbow users
Will render the others lowey losers
And when their power takes the dips
It would be the sign of the apocalypse.

Axel Kemp (11)
Danetree Junior School

My Imagination

My dream is to fly
high in the sky,
as swift as a swallow
that no one can follow.

To give the world peace
and make wars cease,
now people will love
the sky above.

To give everyone a home
and stop people being alone,
make countries join together,
and happiness forever.

Stop hunting on land and sea
let God's creatures roam and swim free
don't harm any creatures
it will spoil other features.

Now the world is a perfect place
we can all sit in grace,
Dear God is this world good?
Have we done what we should?

Lucy Broodbank (10)
Danetree Junior School

Perfect Teacher

I have a perfect teacher
She is kind to me
She smiles in the morning
As happy as can be.
When I am feeling sad and hometime's far away,
She looks at me and smiles and says
'Mummy's on her way.'

Alex Webb (9)
Danetree Junior School

Flowers

Flowers, flowers,
I like flowers,
Roses, tulips,
Lavender and more.

Roses smell of summer,
Tulips of spring,
Snowdrops of winter,
Everybody sing.

Lavender of twilight,
Daffodils of sun,
Poppies of evening
Let's have fun.

Flowers, flowers,
I like flowers
Roses, tulips,
Lavender and more.

Samantha Brooks (8)
Danetree Junior School

Snail Safety

Snails are misunderstood
Because they are covered in slime,
We can't get anywhere quick
It takes us a very long time.

So please take care,
Be aware,
When putting down your feet,
For if you hear a crunching sound,
There will be
A dead snail on the street!

Amy Savage (9)
Danetree Junior School

Rugby, Rugby, Rugby

Rugby, rugby is rough
Rugby, rugby is tough

Robinson, Robinson is so fast
Robinson, Robinson is a blast

Wilko, Wilko scores the kicks
Wilko, Wilko has the tricks

Johnson sometimes has the ball
Johnson is so really tall

Greenwood, Greenwood runs the ball
Greenwood's, Greenwood's passes are cool.

Cohen, Cohen is so fast
Cohen, Cohen always gets past.

Rugby, rugby has a ten minute half
After the match you will need a really big bath!

Dominic Worsley (9)
Danetree Junior School

My Monster!

My monster has curly long hair,
And his large head is the shape of a pear.
My monster has small square eyes,
And his long pink tongue catches lots of flies.
My monster has a big fat belly,
That wobbles and wobbles like strawberry jelly.
My monster's legs are fat and hairy,
And when you see him he's rather scary.
My monster has a red round nose,
And when he lies, it grows and grows.
My monster is frightening, but I think he's great,
Because he is my best mate.

Ashleigh McDowell (9)
Danetree Junior School

I'd Rather Be . . .

I'd rather be a girl than a boy,
I'd rather be a sweet than a toy,
I'd rather be light than dark,
I'd rather be a tent than an ark,
I'd rather be young than old,
I'd rather be hot than cold,
I'd rather be the moon than stars,
I'd rather be Earth than Mars,
I'd rather be rich than poor,
I'd rather have peace than war,
I'd rather be a pencil than a pen,
I'd rather be a chick than a hen,
I'd rather be shy than bold,
I'd rather be warm than cold,
I'd rather have coffee than tea,
Though I'd rather be me!

Emma Hamilton (10)
Danetree Junior School

My Dog Yogi

My dog Yogi has brown eyes,
In summer she likes to catch flies.
She loves to lie in a muddy puddle
But try to bathe her then there's trouble
She's got white fur with a big black spot,
When the doorbell rings she barks a lot.
She's a menace there is no doubt,
She steals my chocolate when we're out.

George Coates (10)
Danetree Junior School

The Dog Show

Dogs fat, dogs small,
Dogs thin, dogs tall.
They come in all different shapes and sizes,
I wonder if my dog will win any prizes.

All the dogs take their places,
Many owners have nervous faces.
The judges come to look and stare,
Their opinions are usually very fair.

Now it's our turn! Off we go
Around the show ring - not too slow!
My little puppy is just swell -
Let's hope that he does really well.

We're patiently waiting for the score.
The judge is coming to the centre of the floor!
Third prize, second prize, we've come first!
I'm so excited, my heart might burst.

Dogs fat, dogs small,
Dogs thin, dogs tall.
They come in all different shapes and sizes,
My little dog has won some prizes!

Ellie Chadwick (10)
Danetree Junior School

It's A Girl Thing

Fashion is such fun, to girls it's like boys with their toy guns.
Shoes, dresses and necklaces, don't forget make-up on your faces.
Do you like dancing, swimming, ballet?
Do you have to clean out your horses' hay?
I bet you like Gucci or even Prada
Do you find maths a lot harder?
When you wash your hair do your curly locks flow?
When you wash it does it glow?
Have you swam with dolphins in the sea?
Have you been friends with Nicole and me?

Stevie Syme (10)
Danetree Junior School

Kids And Clothes

Girls love clothes and clothes love girls
Tops, shorts, any kind
They wear the best that they can find.

Boys love clothes but clothes hate boys
Shirts, shorts, football gear
To the girls they just leer.

Out buying clothes
Is what girls love
They think it's a gift from Heaven above.

Girls love clothes and clothes love girls
And
Boys love clothes but clothes hate boys.

Girls love shopping
Boys are not sure
They think it's just a chore.

Madison Pollard (9)
Danetree Junior School

The Boy From Ewell

There once was a boy from Ewell,
Who didn't like going to school,
He went to the park,
Got eaten by a shark,
And no one missed him at all.

Marc Pryor (9)
Danetree Junior School

Football

Tottenham, Tottenham
They're second from bottom
Robbie Keane, Robbie Keane
He is a scoring machine
Blackburn Rovers, Blackburn Rovers
Round the bend Doncaster Drovers
Dwight Yorke, Dwight Yorke
He has never been called a dork
Wolves, Wolves
They have a lot of footballs
Paul Ince, Paul Ince
He has lots of mints
Real Madrid, Real Madrid
They are always up for a bid
Carlos, Carlos
He comes from Panathinaikos
Lyon, Lyon
They always get on
Irkpa, Irkpa
He has a friend called Philla.

Nathan Stovell (9)
Danetree Junior School

Once Upon A Rhyme

Little Red Riding Hood
I bet she is really good
Or is she bad?
Does she drive you mad?
Does she bully
In her lovely warm woolly?
Does she cry
In a blink of an eye
Or is she just like you and me
And likes to picnic under a tree?

Humpty Dumpty sat on a wall
We know what happened
He had a great fall.
Broke his shell
What a smell!
Wish he'd fallen down a well
The king's horses all felt sick
The king's men poked him with a stick
They scraped him up
And as you see
They all had scrambled egg for tea!

Little Bo-Peep
You know the one
She lost her sheep
Just for fun
High and low she looked for them
Around the hill and back again
Nowhere were they to be seen
People laughed, they were so mean.
Little Bo-Peep went home to bed
Her sheep were there inside the shed!

Ashleigh Kidd (9)
Danetree Junior School

Things That Make Me Feel Happy

A walk in the park,
Bright lights in the dark,
Burgers and chips,
Doritos and dips,
A cuddle from Mummy
And sweets for my tummy,
The things that make me feel happy.

A day out with Dad
A nice-looking lad
Music and singing,
A good time that's blingin'.
The things that make me feel happy.

So my message to you is when you feel blue,
Think of things that make you feel happy.

Georga Davies (10)
Danetree Junior School

Winter

Snow, snow I love the snow
Snow on the car, places to go.
Slipping, sliding on the ice
Which I think is rather nice.

I love the snow and the crunchy sound
When walking on the frozen ground
Slipping, sliding on the ice
Which I think is rather nice.

Snow on the mountains
And frozen fountains
Slipping sliding on the ice
Which I think is rather
            Nice.

Maisie Grant
Danetree Junior School

I Like . . .

I like to dance,
I like to play,
I like to swim,
And go on holiday.

I like the sun,
I like the snow,
I like the rain,
It helps things grow.

I like cats,
I like dogs,
I'm not too sure
If I like frogs.

I like blue,
I like red,
I like to spend,
The day in bed.

I like rice,
I like curry,
I like McDonald's,
And a Crunchie McFlurry.

I like Fanta,
I like lemonade,
I like Coke,
And cherryade.

I love Dad
I love Mum
I love my family
They're so much fun.

Leanne Cook (10)
Danetree Junior School

Homework

My mum is looking sad
I'm driving her so mad
I won't sit down to write
She's been asking all the night.

Mum's going mad again
I'm driving her insane
My homework page is plain
Homework is a pain!

My teacher said go home
And write a lovely poem
But ideas they just won't come
Am I the only one?

Drew Anderson (10)
Danetree Junior School

The Playground

In the playground people were shouting
In the playground people were arguing
In the playground people were shouting
Because they scored a goal.
In the playground people are playing hopscotch.
People are playing rugby, throwing the ball.
People are chasing each other, getting out of breath.
Our playground is noisy but fun.

Jamie Workman (8)
Danetree Junior School

The Wind

I'm lying in my bed at night
The wind is howling out of sight.
Where does it go?
I don't know.
To the moon and back?
Or round the North Pole?
To France or Spain
Or through the nearest black hole?

I listen to the trees,
The wind is whipping through the leaves.
I hear a noise, it's the wind whimpering,
It suddenly feels cold and I'm shivering.
The wind's died down
All is still
Where has it gone?
It's left a chill.

Nicole Green (10)
Danetree Junior School

Spring

The grass is swaying in the breeze
The old oak tree is sprouting leaves
The blossoms on the trees all ready
The sunflowers are growing tall and steady.

Bunnies hopping 'to' and 'fro'
A newborn owl swooping low,
A new chick pecking corn,
And eagles flying through till dawn.

The frost makes way for windy days
The sun is peeping through the haze,
The raindrops all die away,
It makes way for summery days.

Hannah Shephard (9)
Danetree Junior School

The Cat's Open Eyes

The cat stares and glares
at a wondrous sight.
It lays and stays, walks
and talks and has ray-grey silver stripes,
As the cat gazes in wonder.

A small dog appeared out of the dark,
shadowy night.
The dog scared the cat from the shadow above.
As she hid under some bronze painted logs.
She winked at the dog and said, 'Can we be friends
after what happened to us?'
The dog softly barked,
And they became friends.
And they had a very happy time.

Melissa French (9)
Danetree Junior School

The Buzzing Bee In Winter

One day in the snow,
I spotted a crow,
On top of a tree,
Right by a buzzing bee.

I hopped on my sleigh,
And put it away,
Then it was time for tea,
And in came the buzzing bee.

Then I went to bed
And to my mum I said
'I hope it snows tomorrow
Then I won't feel any sorrow.'

Nicole Holloway (9)
Danetree Junior School

I Love Horses

Cantering and trotting,
All around the sand school,
Riding on the horses,
It's really, really cool.

Lots of different types,
Running all around,
With Arabs, Shetland, Palomino,
Their feet hardly touch the ground.

Shadow is my favourite,
I don't know of his breed,
But still I love to ride him,
And walk him by the lead.

Showjumping and dressage,
Are different types of shows,
Dressing up the horses,
With pretty little bows.

Ride them in the winter,
Ride them in the fall
'Cause when it comes to horse riding
I love it best of all.

Lorna Dicken (9)
Danetree Junior School

The Train

The train is waking up,
It is being cleaned out,
The driver has a bucket
And is very, very stout.

The train is going along,
Sometimes it whistles and sometimes it poops,
The driver always sings a song,
While athletes jump through hoops.

The train is at the station,
It waits for all its friends,
While the driver sees his relation,
The track is straight but sometimes bends.

The train is never late back,
Even if it's raining hard,
The driver puts on his rain mac,
While the train goes past the scrapyard.

The station is in sight,
And the sky is very dark,
The train strains with all its might,
While it passes by the park.

The train arrives in the shed,
It is feeling very weak,
Now it is time for bed,
Next to Mallard who is very sleek.

Daniel Underwood (10)
Danetree Junior School

Teachers

Teachers teaching literacy, teachers teaching maths
For lunch they always go down to the café.
Teachers teaching in my school
Make up the following rules.
Teachers wide, teachers thin
Some of them couldn't come in.
Teachers small, teachers tall
They really are a know-it-all.
Teachers nice, teachers mad
Teachers don't like it when you're sad.
Teachers clever, teachers bright,
They always snore in the night.
Teachers loony, teachers happy
Teachers really, really moody.
Sit down quietly now, now, now
Don't make a noise or row.
Keep your hands, feet and objects to yourself.
In science they make us learn about health.

Katherine Amer (9)
Danetree Junior School

The Magic Hat

I had a magic hat,
It came with a baseball bat.
I tried out my magic hat,
Then I pulled out a cat.
I put away my hat,
I took out my hat the other day,
In the month of May.
With my hat I lay
On that sunny beach bay.
I did tricks,
While I was only six.

Harry Wales (9)
Danetree Junior School

My Pen

My pen is red, green and yellow
Every time I use it I have to say hello
To the ink that seeps and stains my fingers,
And work, oh what a pain.

My pen is red, green and yellow,
Not pink and fluffy like marshmallow.
The writing on my work is always smudging
And people next to me are always nudging.

My pen is red, green and yellow,
Using it always makes me feel mellow.
I'm so thankful for my pen from Santa
I'm glad I left him a glass of Fanta!

Richard Teare (9)
Danetree Junior School

My Sister Hayley

My sister Hayley is terribly lazy,
She never gets out of bed.
When you shout at her early in the morning,
She doesn't even raise her head.

I'm her sister, Jamie-Lee and, she certainly doesn't take
after me!
When she comes home she has a big moan and all
she wants is her tea.

Jamie-Lee Duffell (9)
Danetree Junior School

The Lord Of The Rings

Legolas with his bow and arrows,
and his two small daggers, he is an elf.

Aragorn with his bow and arrows and
long sword to save himself.

Gimli the dwarf, with his axe,
he kills everything in his path.

Gandalf the wizard with his magic staff.

Frodo the one with the ring and
he's trying to get to the Dark Lord.

Sam, Frodo's protector and bag carrier,
his only weapon, a sword.

Matthew Halls (9)
Danetree Junior School

What Spiders Are Really Like

Itchy, stingy, hairy
Extremely lairy.
I make people wary.
You will find me far and near
Or sucking the blood of a deer!
Dangerous spiders and calm spiders,
Don't bother trying to find us.
If you see a spider climbing out from the pipe
Don't go Mummy! And get a wipe.
Just quickly get out
Before you get a bite!

Levente Green (9)
Danetree Junior School

My Cat Bubbles

I don't know much about my cat called Bubbles
But I'll tell you what I do.

Firstly she was a girl not a boy,
And I never treated her like a toy.
Secondly she was black and not white,
Mostly she purred all night.
Thirdly she was a playful little cat,
She always seemed to bite my grandad Pat.
Fourth, she was mischevious that's for certain
Always pulling down our curtains.
Fifth, she liked fish not the meat
She always finished by licking her feet.
Sixth, I always remember her red collar and bell,
Always causing Mum and Dad hell.
Seventh, she always licked her bowl clean,
To the tomcats she was mean.
Eighth, I seemed to remember her getting old,
She had a heart of gold.
Ninth, as time passed, she got weaker,
Sleek and slender, mild and sleepier.
Tenth, finally she ran away
We thought she might come back someday.
Three years on, she's still not returned, I miss her loads.

Natasha Inns (9)
Danetree Junior School

The Puppy

My puppy is a happy chap
He barks and barks and yelps
And when I get really upset
He comes along and helps.

Emma Penn (6)
Downsway School

I'm So Dizzy

Dear Maureen,
I am fresh water
Every day I go somewhere dark
Then I go down the loo.
I hate getting cleaned
I get clay in my hair
I go up and down pipes
It makes me really dizzy,
Then when I get poured into a cup,
I go everywhere.
Then I end up on the floor,

Yours so dizzy
Fizzy.

Ashley Jones (11)
Green Wrythe Primary School

Help Meee!

Dear Maureen,
Today is the day that I leave,
Because I am the air.
I go up and I go down
Sometimes I go round and round.
No one can see me
They always hit me,
And I get tangled up in a tree.
I can't get down
I get eaten by a hound
And now I can never be found.

Yours worriedly,
Wooshy.

Chloe Pearson-Fletcher (10)
Green Wrythe Primary School

Dog Limericks

There was a small dog with a flea
He decided to climb up a tree.
The flea began to bite,
The dog took a fright
And they both fell out of the tree.

There was a young dog called Billy
He acted really silly.
He chased his tail,
He barked at a whale
And that's why they call him Silly Billy.

There was a dog called Brandy
She enjoyed a big drink of shandy.
She got really drunk,
She bumped into a skunk,
And now they call her smelly Brandy.

Amanda Wessier (10)
Green Wrythe Primary School

Dear Maureen

I am a weak old jelly
I wobble all day and night
Every day at 6.15
The blobbers eat a bit of me
Oh help! Oh help! Oh help me please!
How can I get away?
What shall I do?
Why, oh why must this happen?

Yours wobble and woe,
Wubble the raspberry jelly.

Richard Gregory (11)
Green Wrythe Primary School

A Minute Till Nine O'Clock

A minute till nine o'clock and I'm in bed
And these are the things I think about:
The ghosts that hoot at me through my window,
The door swinging side to side
And the footsteps creeping up the stairs,
And then I think of my future ahead,
Will I be an astronaut, a lawyer or even the next Michael Jordan?

One minute till ten o'clock and I'm still up
And these are the things I think about:
I think of the toy that's still hanging out of my sister's window
And is there really a neck slitter under my bed?
I also think of going to the beach
For an everlasting holiday.
Or maybe I might see America's next president.

Joshua Ogenji (11)
Green Wrythe Primary School

A Minute To Nine O'Clock

A minute to nine o'clock and I am in my bed
And these are the things I like about:
Bunny rabbits,
Cuddly dogs, dancing on stage,
Things about my footie, then I see a shadow on the wall.
Thinking about the hairy monster under my bed.
Becoming lost under my covers
I can hear the trees outside blowing
I can hear footsteps.

Jessica Pryor (10)
Green Wrythe Primary School

Dogs Go Woof, Woof

Dogs go woof, woof in the middle of the night
Dogs go woof, woof and it gives us a fright
That is right.

They eat bones all day long
And then they start to sing this song.

Dogs go woof, woof in the middle of the night
Dogs go woof, woof and it gives us a fright.

They're a man's best friend
Until the very end.

Dogs go woof, woof in the middle of the night
Dogs go woof, woof and it gives us a fright.

Danielle Mulvenna (10)
Green Wrythe Primary School

I Am Gorge!

I am gorge when I get out of bed in the morning.
I am gorge even though I'm yawning.
I am gorge when I am crunching on my cornflakes.
I am gorge when I lick the icing off the fairy cakes.
I am gorge when I laugh at the boys in my class.
I am gorge though when the teacher said 'Where is Emily Gorge?'
All the boys said 'Pass.'
I am gorge when all the wind hits my face.
I am gorge and totally *not* a disgrace.
See it is what inside you that counts, not on your skin?

Emily McDonnell (11)
Green Wrythe Primary School

Down Behind The Dustbin

Down behind the dustbin
I met a dog called Jim.
'Leave me alone' he says,
'I'm feeling very glim.'

Down behind the dustbin
I met a girl called Millie.
'She lives with a friend' I said
'And his name is Billy.'

Down behind the dustbin
I met a fish called Bubble.
'She loves to swim in water' I said
'And she's never in trouble.'

Jorden Poulton (11)
Green Wrythe Primary School

A Minute To Nine O'Clock

A minute to nine o'clock and I'm in bed
And these are the things I think about:
I think of the creaky noise under my bed,
A scary clown waiting to get me when my foot goes down,
And also my future being a beautician.

A minute to nine I'm still up
And these are the things about:
A shadow running round in circles,
Oh! It's only my mum!

Tucker Davey (11)
Green Wrythe Primary School

Guess What?

I'm in my bed at night
When the stars are bright
I hear a creak outside my door
It's my dog chewing a ball on the floor
Then he chews up my socks,
He chews up my shoes
So I put him outside,
Cos the back garden's wide.

I went back upstairs
And went back to bed
And had a dream about peaches and ice cream.
I woke up yawning and it wasn't morning,
Suddenly . . . I put on the light and had a great fright,
Cos it was the middle of the night.
I looked back outside of my bedroom door
It was my cat chewing my welcome mat.
So I said 'No' and let him out and said 'Goodbye.'

So I couldn't go back to sleep
So I had a peep at the dog outside,
You won't want to know
He's chewing my sister's slide.

You won't want to know
The next minute he's back inside
Chewing my sister's Teletubbies Po.
One year later the dog and cat were chewing the ball
On the floor, also
My welcome mat and my socks and my shoes
Plus a new thing, a rat!

Lauren Powis (11)
Green Wrythe Primary School

My Son Put Me On The Transfer List

On offer:
One good cook, thirty-three years old
Tidies your room for you
Helps you with your homework
But can shout a lot
Grounds you for months
This is a *free transfer!*
She also comes with running expenses
Needs to eat lots of
Burgers, beans, apples,
Vodka, beer, chips,
Veg, corn, dips,
And endless packets of chewing gum.
She can be nice,
I'll have her back after the football
Only until the tennis starts,
Any takers?

Steven Dance (11)
Green Wrythe Primary School

Flower

There was a flower
And he had all the power
There was light
And he was bright
Sometimes he would have a good shower.

Danielle Staff (10)
Green Wrythe Primary School

Dream On!

A minute to ten o'clock and I'm in bed
And these are the things I think about:

Like playing for Chelsea and scoring a hat-trick
against Manchester United
Getting grabbed by the ankle grabber,
Getting robbed by Scream
Also being the richest person in the world
Being in a street race down Mount Everest,
Having the biggest chocolate cake fight in the world,
Owning Stamford Bridge and living in luxury.

A minute to eleven o'clock and I'm still awake
And these are the things I think about:

Running the London Marathon and winning a gold medal,
Bungee-jumping off the Eiffel Tower
Never having to go to school and being allowed to eat
the biggest bar of chocolate in one
Then I woke up and had breakfast.

Craig Hart (10)
Green Wrythe Primary School

There Once Was A Man Called Jim

There once was a man called Jim
Who decided to go for a swim
He jumped in the pool
And acted all cool
And then he began to sing.

Kyle Duffin (10)
Green Wrythe Primary School

My Mum's On The Transfer List

On offer:
One good cook, thirty six years old
Is good with the ironing
And spends all of her money on you
Knows how to clear up after people
But she does stay out late every night
And she is a heavy smoker.
This is a *free transfer!*
But she does come with running expenses
Weeks of shopping and loving
Burberry bags and fags, and loads of Blue WKD.
Needs huge amounts of
Food and vodka, a car and money
Jewellery and a job, clothes and dieting tablets
And endless packs of chewing gum.
This offer is open until late August
At least until her birthday is,
Any takers?

Tyler Chambers (11)
Green Wrythe Primary School

Limerick

There was an old kangaroo
Who baked like a tiger too
He danced around
And fell on the ground
And then he caught the flu.

Luke Brown (11)
Green Wrythe Primary School

Dear Maureen

Dear Maureen,
I am a piece of bubblegum
Every day after school
A gang of girls
Who are really cool
Come and tread on me
And start screaming
So by four o'clock
I have a headache
And a very bad back.

Yours tatterly
Bob Bubblegum.

Carina Lamelas (10)
Green Wrythe Primary School

Dead Wedding

A woman from Cape Town got wed
To a guy who was already dead
The trouble did start
When he stopped his own heart
And something fell out of his head.

Antonio Evans Godoy (10)
Green Wrythe Primary School

There Once Was A Man Called Jon

There once was a man called Jon
Who jumped off a plane in Hong Kong
He was a canary
Who had a fairy
And that was the end of Jon.

Jamie Fallows (10)
Green Wrythe Primary School

Minute To Midnight

Minute to midnight I am still awake
I hear noises outside in the night.
I hear the barking, the cats purring,
The lamp posts flickering
The wind howling
The trees swishing
The rains grin.

Daniel Townsend (10)
Green Wrythe Primary School

The Young Man From Surrey

There once was a young man from Surrey
Who went to the shop for a curry
He wanted a drink,
His face went bright pink
Because of the heat of the curry.

Adam Barker (11)
Green Wrythe Primary School

My School Is The Best Of All

My school is the best of all,
All the teachers are nice,
All the teachers are cool,
My school is the best of all.

My school is the best of all,
Mr Hollingsworth is our head.
He makes sure all the pencils have lead
My school is the best of all.

My school is the best of all
Miss Ridley is the year leader,
Because she is a very good reader,
My school is the best of all.

My school is the best of all,
Emily is my best friend,
But she doesn't live in Send
My school is the best of all.

Alice Hudson (9)
Northmead Junior School

January Mornings

Misty fog,
Creeps along the lane,
Flaky strips of paint,
Blown from the windowpane.

The frost,
That bites into your neck,
Turning you into a
Weak old wreck.

Catherine Boyton (7)
Northmead Junior School

The Old Man

There was an old man
Who had a big van
He had grey hair
And his tummy was bare.

He had a weird house
With a tiny old mouse
He had loads of money
So he bought a sweet bunny.

He went to town
Dressed like a clown
He walked like a duck
And was covered in muck.

There's my imaginary dad
Do you think he's mad?

Sherelyn Norcliffe (9)
Northmead Junior School

My Piano

My piano is my friend in many different ways
When I am playing a merry old tune
It's like a good friend listening
Encouraging me to play more
When I'm trying to learn a difficult tune
It's like my teacher,
Helping me with the notes
But best of all, it is a friend
Who congratulates when I've done well
So as you can see,
My piano is definitely my friend.

Rhiannon Lloyd (8)
Northmead Junior School

Plane Sights

Flying high,
Into the sky,
A very high height
Very few sights.

The giddiness of take-off
The clouds so soft
Gathering round
Without a sound.

Then down from the sky
The plane will fly
All of the clouds
In the crowds . . .
Gone!

Jessica Boyton (9)
Northmead Junior School

My Puppy

My puppy is the cutest pup
That you will ever see,
Her name is Mocha
And she loves to sleep on your knee.
Before we got her the argument
Was what we were to call her,
I thought Abby, my sister Holly,
I don't know how we got to Mocha!
Mocha is a great name,
'Cause she is a coffee-brown
She looks at you with her round hazel eyes,
That you just can't turn her down.
Mocha is so very sweet,
And I love oh so much,
She really gives our family,
That special final touch!

Hannah Nicholas (11)
St Catherine's Preparatory School, Bramley

The Winter's Path

As I walk along the cold winter path,
I hear families in their houses
Sitting by the fire,
The trees surround me like low fog,
The moon looks through the trees
As if it is staring at me,
I can hear the horses' feet on the cobblestone road
While the silver spider's web clings to the stars,
On a cold winter's night.

I come across a blackbird
With its left wing broken,
Deserted,
On a cold winter's night.

Ahead I go
No one around me,
A man appears
In front of me,
I am startled
Just like the blackbird,
On a cold winter's night.

Caitlin Parker (11)
St Catherine's Preparatory School, Bramley

The Cat

The carefree cat,
With his sharp teeth and claws,
Can do what he likes,
Whether it is hunting for mice
Or dozing on a branch.

The moon will sail on above him,
And the sun will ignore his presence,
But down on Earth, below the stars,
A mouse runs on and on.

It keeps running and running,
But the cat's eyes can see it in the dark.
There is nowhere to hide
The cat will find it eventually
There is nowhere to hide.

But wait, there is one place
Inside a wall a cat cannot reach,
For it is too large to get in the hole
The mouse runs inside
It has escaped, but the cat's yellow eyes
Will forever haunt its dreams.

Lizzie Corrie (10)
St Catherine's Preparatory School, Bramley

A Wish

Walking on the Downs,
The wind rushing through the grass,
Dogs are running with joy,
But they belong to other people,
How I wish one was mine.

Walking through the street,
The cars zoooooom around the corner,
Dogs walk, not free to run,
But they belong to other people,
How I wish one was mine.

Walking with such pride,
The first steps up the hill,
Dogs pass and look with interest,
But they belong to other people,
This one belongs to *me!*

Ella Davies (11)
St Catherine's Preparatory School, Bramley

An Autumn's Day

The bare autumn trees swayed in the strong
threatening wind
Leaves as crisp as toast began to spin.
The calm, sweet birds started to sing as the local
church bells began to ring.
Dark cotton wool balls started to roll across the
bright blue sky, as everyone disappointedly sighed
Splishing and sploshing the rain began to contentedly
fall to the ground
As the birds stooped and made no sound.
Autumn is going and winter is approaching.
The animals will disappear as the snow will begin
to fall as white as dust.

Joanna Hitchcock (11)
St Catherine's Preparatory School, Bramley

Matilda The Builder

Matilda was a builder
With a bright pink van
You'd see her on top of scaffolding
With a hammer in her hand.
Nails in her orange overalls and pencils in her hair,
Every time she went to site everyone would stare.

Matilda was a builder
With a bright pink van
She worked outside all year round,
And got a Mediterranean tan.
She could fix any window and mend any door
But everything had to stop for a cup of tea at four.

Matilda was a builder
With a bright pink van
She could build any tower
And a bridge of any span.
She could dig a deep foundation, until the day was done
As long as it stayed dry, so her nail varnish wouldn't run.

Matilda was a builder
With a bright pink van
She would decorate your dining room
And mix the concrete with sand.
She could plaster any ceiling, filling every crack
But be sure you pay her well, if you want her to come back.

Frances Bird (11)
St Catherine's Preparatory School, Bramley

Once Upon A Rhyme

Once upon a rhyme,
A long, long time ago
Little Lucy Goodsniff
Was doing up her bow.

She was going out to school,
It was her very first day.
But when she finally got there,
She did not want to play.

All the other boys and girls
Were running round the room.
But she just sat there quietly,
And time was going zoom.

The next day when she got to school,
She had a talk to the teacher.
The other girls were bullying her
About her prominent feature.

It was not her fault her nose was so large,
It went back through the ages.
Her mother, father, grandmother too,
Further in history's pages.

The next day was just like any other
And Lucy was sitting alone
She suddenly smelt a smoky smell,
And left her plastic phone.

A fire was burning in the other room
Lucy had smelt it well
She managed to get everyone one out.
And then she sounded the bell.

Ellie Buchanan (11)
St Catherine's Preparatory School, Bramley

The Hard Done-By Cat

First 'she' turned on the light,
And kicked me from the chair

The computer was turned on,
I was greeted by a flashing hare.

The 'baby elephant' came stomping downstairs
Turned on the Gamecube - stupid thing.

So I retreated to a nice cosy pile of washing,
They removed me later, by starting to sing.

I sulked back to the airing cupboard
And at last fell asleep on a dress.

Only to be chased around the house,
For making such a mess!

Emily Marmion (10)
St Catherine's Preparatory School, Bramley

The Whale

Oh whale come to me
On the water, on the sea
Spray your water up to the sky
Until you are nearly dry.

I give you food
If you're in a good mood
You are a deep blue
That colour is you.

I lay this flower on the seabed
To keep me forever in your head
I will always remember
You as Amber.

Zoe Geidelberg (10)
St Catherine's Preparatory School, Bramley

Wolf

The grey wolf's teeth
Glisten in the light,
The running rabbit,
Wishes for flight.

He sprints after the rabbit
His tail like lace,
The rabbit's exhaustion
Hangs in its face.

The rabbit stops,
His time is done,
But the wolf's fun
Has just begun.

As the wolf finishes
He stands up tall,
The blood on his lips
Is covered in drool.

The wolf lies down,
Then hears a bang,
He looks at his chest
And feels a pang.

The bloodstained grass
Droops with the weight,
And the wolf's heart
Fills with hate.

Victoria Rea (10)
St Catherine's Preparatory School, Bramley

The Elephant's Dream

The elephant packed his trunk one day
He had decided to go on holiday
But heaven forbid, where do you go
When you're a ginormous fat hefalump
And even your toes won't fit in a train
Your trunk is so large it hangs out the plane!

This elephant's wish was to swim with the fish
In the land of Didgeridoo,
Now Didgeridoo is a magical place
Full of pixies and elves,
Surrounded by water and very soft sand
An elephant's paradise had been found.

Poor old elephant he didn't travel well
Stuck in the jungle
With a terrible smell, a wife that nagged
And a baby that yelled.

So sad he was, and all upset
He decided to go and clear his head.
He trudged through the jungle and crossed
the stream
Until finally he came across a pond
Full of golden fish
His one great wish.

Emma Dane (10)
St Catherine's Preparatory School, Bramley

Wind

There is wind that comes to England
Wind that skips to Spain,
But the wind I love the most
Is wind that rustles leaves
And tousles my hair.

Breeze is warm and gentle,
Blusts are cold and rough
Air is calm and still and soothing
Perfect for hot, baking summer days.

The north wind is freezing and heavy-laden with snow
The south wind is warm and moist, bringing mist.
The west wind is chilled and damp,
But the east wind is cool and fresh,
Clearing your mind of worries.

There is wind that turns round and round
Wind that tears up houses and trees,
Wind that makes a thunderous sound,
A hurricane's eye that never sees.

Wind is a dragon,
Frightening the clouds, forcing them to
Scatter and flee.
Wind is a faithful dog
Comforting, relaxing,
But above all, it is
The breath of life.

Emma Charatan (10)
St Catherine's Preparatory School, Bramley

A Winter's Tail

Footprints in the snow
Pawprints staining the spotless white sheet.

Small movements in the snow,
Snuffling, scratching, scrabbling.

A small Westie, hiding in the snow,
Part of the endless world of white.

Snow starts falling rapidly,
Nowhere to go, lost in a big duvet of brilliant white.

Scrabbling starts again, frantically trying to get away from the cold,
Picked up by someone, the dog is rescued from an icy cave.

Through the treacherous blizzard, fighting to move a tiny step,
Home again, next to the blazing fire, hot cocoa and a blanket.

The dog has no owner, an orphan.
Sad, waiting for his true owner to come back.

Waiting, tail wagging with hope
Nothing, no icy steps along the gravel path.

Scratching at the door, trying to get out,
To find his owner on his own.

Out on a walk, the dog barks. Nothing.
Not a cry of joy, not a thing.

A scent in the air, caught in his nose
Could it be?

Racing along the blanket of fluff,
Still chasing the scent of his owner.

A tall man, with a lead and a smile on his face,
Is filled with delight as he dog sees him and races over.

Joy, a happy face, the man who found his dog,
Sadness, a new friend, perhaps, lost, the man who rescued the dog.

Left on his own, no friends,
Nothing except the endless stretch of white.

Helena Muir (10)
St Catherine's Preparatory School, Bramley

The Great Poet Of Amherst

How tiny and feeble she looks
She writes all day and all night
Maybe this is why she has two books
That she always holds tight.

She inhabits a hole only fit for one mouse
The Great Poet of Amherst
She has learned to make it her home, her house
Anywhere else would have been worse.

The one danger, while working
In this mouse house of thought
That is the cat may be lurking
Behind any corner and the Great Mouse of Amherst may be caught.

A friend she has made
Emily was her name
And everynight, before sunset poems of thought and feeling
Is what they would trade
And this would go on 'til morning came.

The Great Poet of Amherst, you see
Was nothing but a mouse
Who lived with her friend, Emily
In a little mouse house.

Philippa Heggie (10)
St Catherine's Preparatory School, Bramley

My Kittens

My kittens like to play around
They are so very sweet
They bump and jump all over the place
And they like to get my feet!

My kittens like to laze around
Dreaming by the fire
But they claw and rip all the carpets up
To their hearts' desire.

My kittens like to wander around
As if they own the place
They walk in and out of all the rooms
To find their special space.

My kittens like to run around
They catch the birds and mice
But when they finally come inside
They pretend they're really nice!

My kittens and I love each other
So when I'm feeling sad
They're always there to cuddle me
Until I'm feeling glad.

Sophie Johnson (11)
St Catherine's Preparatory School, Bramley

Once Upon A Rhyme

Far, far back in time
There was this little rhyme:

Hey diddle, diddle,
Man is as fit as a fiddle
He could easily jump over the moon,
His little dog laughed to see such fun
And Neil Armstrong ran away with the spoon.

Flushed with success,
From his recent excess,
He and his beagle
Would mimic the eagle,
And jump to a planet beyond.

The red star did glow
And desire did grow
To find life in the black of the night.
He and his beagle set off as an eagle
To give those Martians a fright.

Jennifer Salvage (11)
St Catherine's Preparatory School, Bramley

The Midnight Fox

The midnight fox
comes out at night
if he sees another fox
he puts up a fight.

He may look cute
to the naked eye
but if he sees a coot
that coot will die.

The midnight fox
won't bear the light
when the sun comes up
he's not in sight.

Hannah Church (10)
St Catherine's Preparatory School, Bramley

The Pied Piper's Regrets

I was a piper, young and free,
When I came to Hamelin Town,
You, the Mayor, you cheated me,
And I in turn hurt thee.

First I took the deadly rats
To the river's brink.
Then I piped and piped, and piped some more
And caused them all to sink.

Well, I thought, Mr Mayor,
It was not quite fair
You refused to pay me what you owed
And so the magic pipe I blowed.

I took them up the mountainside,
I took them to the top,
They struggled on - with me in front,
I would not let them stop.

So you see Mr Mayor, I am so sorry,
All those children make me worry,
Some are grey and all are old,
Some are dead and most are cold.

Now I realise I was wrong,
To take them all away,
I'm truly sorry, oh yes I am,
I live in shame each day!

Anna Drummond (11)
St Catherine's Preparatory School, Bramley

Alone

As I stand alone, sad, small,
I stand on my own.
As I stand alone, wishing I was tall,
I stand on my own.

I stand alone, courage waning,
I stand on my own.
As I stand alone, courage gaining,
I stand on my own.

As I stand alone, hoping, deciding,
I stand on my own.
As I stand alone, I've made up my mind,
I stand on my own.

As I walk along, shy, scared,
I walk on my own.
As I come to think, why had I dared?
I walk on my own.

I walked up to them, stumbling, quaking,
I walked on my own.
I walked up to them, my hands shaking,
I walked on my own.

I pleaded to them, a stutter in my voice,
I pleaded on my own.
'May I be your friend?' Was this really my choice?
I pleaded on my own.

They smiled at me with curious laughter.
No longer on my own.
When I think back now, now it's over.
Why was I so slow?

Anna Jordan (11)
St Catherine's Preparatory School, Bramley

Exams

Finished the paper,
Checked it times three.
Out in the park
Is where I should be!

I look at my watch,
Five minutes left.
Why should I bother
With this stupid test?

I can't wait for the moment
When the examiner says
'Alright, put your pens down,
We've finished the test.'

Only two minutes left now
Oh yes! Hooray!
I won't sit another test
'Til the SATs in May.

All hot and sweaty,
Watching the clock.
Falling asleep,
Oh, when will this stop?

Phew! It's all over,
No more tests 'til May!
Now I can leave
And go out to play.

I hate Common Entrance,
It's such a bore.
But when I get home
I'll get cuddles galore!

Sophie Reid (11)
St Catherine's Preparatory School, Bramley

Different Sweets

Looking at the different sweets,
Is so tempting for me,
The chocolate sweets,
The chewy sweets,
The sherbet staring at me.

The gum all gooey and soft,
The fruit pastilles in my hands,
And look at this,
My favourite one,
The greatest one on the land.

Fudge and Dream melt in my mouth,
A feeling I've felt before.
The pic 'n' mix
The lollipops
I'll love them evermore.

Victoria Jefferies (10)
St Catherine's Preparatory School, Bramley

River Air

The pleasant evening air
Rippling on the water.
Dancing in the moonlight
Flowing in the open space.

Picking up speed now,
Whistling in the willow,
Snapping at the grass,
And scratching at the river bed.

Slowing right down,
Stop.
Silent, still and silver.

Soon nothing to be seen
Plain, smooth and empty.
The night has fallen.

Zoe Clarke (11)
St Catherine's Preparatory School, Bramley

Fish

Dark, blank eyes
Musty, warm water.
Dust swirls,
Fish rolls along,
Searching the wet,
For food.
Searching for shade,
A dark shadow getting larger,
Fish goes to it,
Looks up,
Feels fear,
Flicks away,
A shining spark of sun,
Lost,
Squelch,
Sees a red cloud,
Sharp pain,
Then nothing.

Catherine Hall (11)
St Catherine's Preparatory School, Bramley

A Walk In The Countryside

Hair blowing,
Eyes stinging,
Grass swaying,
Struggling on.

> Steep valleys,
> Dark forests,
> Large puddles,
> Standing strong.

Home at last,
Up to bed
Tucked up tight,
Awake too long!
Yawwwn!

Francesca MacVean (11)
St Catherine's Preparatory School, Bramley

The Jaguar

Sleek and silent, brave and bold,
Slinking gently through the trees,
Eyes of gold and teeth of pearls,
Running swiftly through the trees.
Sunset fur and midnight spots
Slowly stopping by the trees.
Claws that twinkle like the stars,
Climbing nimbly up a tree.
So swift, so sleek,
So full of grace, so elegant,
That is what a jaguar is.

Maria Pluzhnikov (10)
St Catherine's Preparatory School, Bramley

Dolphins

As they glide
As they jump
As they jump over the hump,
As they splash,
Among the waves,
So slippery,
So smooth,
As it swims,
Waves crash around,
As it swims softly to land.

Isabel Healy (10)
St Catherine's Preparatory School, Bramley

Beware!

As the monkeys swing from tree to tree,
The parrots chatter joyfully,
The sloth yawns but doesn't wake,
As the antelope leaps . . . big mistake.
For as the king waits and stares,
This antelope should say his prayers.
Suddenly the antelope's gone,
Obviously the king has won,
The gentle hissing of a snake,
As the other animals gradually wake,
Is no match for the lion's roar,
As he wanders around the jungle floor.

Sophie Oakes (10)
St Catherine's Preparatory School, Bramley

An Elephant

An elephant
The largest living land mammal
Gentle, huge, active
A tall tank crushing trees as it goes through the jungle,
As friendly as a baby,
As heavy as a load of lead,
A lovely creature soon to be extinct,
As kind as a mother,
An elephant,
It has a jewel which twinkles like a star in your eyes.

Gaby Custance (10)
St Catherine's Preparatory School, Bramley

A Dog

The dog loudly barks
In the beautiful park
He runs as quick as a shiver
And his fur is as shiny as silver
He is white, brown and long-haired
But the fur at his feet, flared.
He barks at the ducks gliding over the pond
But they just ignore and go waddling on
Now tied up to the tree
Watching a bumblebee
He feels very left out
When suddenly his owner shouts
'Let's go home and have some tea'
He is now finally free!
He feels great!

Alice Facey (10)
St Catherine's Preparatory School, Bramley

Gone With The Wind

He gallops along the river
never stopping to drink.
Going so fast you would
miss him in a blink.
Galloping further and further
far away from home.
There was no one there to save him
as he fell over down to the ground.

Everything went still
nothing more but black
nothing there at all
now he could never go back.

Hannah Johnson (11)
St Catherine's Preparatory School, Bramley

No Answer

I called for her, watching for her shadow,
No answer
I ran, still calling in the wet meadow,
No answer.
I ran, clutching her scarf tightly,
No answer.
I thought of the old times, how we were,
No answer.
I thought of where she might be now,
No answer.
I thought I saw her, but alas it was a cow,
No answer.
I saw the sun and knew it was time to go home,
No answer.
I woke in the morning only to find her comb,
No answer.
What has happened to Emily, my darling baby horse?

Megan Spalding (10)
St Catherine's Preparatory School, Bramley

Feeling Nervous

Fingers trembling, knees shaking, in my spleen feel vomit making.
Face is red, brow is knitted, costume is too tightly fitted.
Should I make out that I'm sick? If I do, I'll do it quick.
No point now, the curtain's drawn, Now I'm feeling quite forlorn.
Lights are glaring, overbearing. I am waiting, people staring.
My time is near and now it's clear, I can't remember why I'm here!
Ah! I've remembered, 'Apples! Apples! Get your apples!' Applause!

Katy David (11)
St Catherine's Preparatory School, Bramley

My Life

One night when I went to bed
I heard a big bang in my head
I realised my bed was flying
What a beautiful view
As I flew over you

As I flew into my dreams
I flew quickly into space
I looked down and thought
What a happy place
As I flew over you

When I looked closer
I could see my house and school
I could see my family and friends
I miss them
As I flew over you.

I want to return from space
Back to this beautiful and happy place
Then suddenly I am awake
And realise how lucky I am
As I flew over you.

Georgina Disney-May (9)
St Catherine's Preparatory School, Bramley

Boring Rainy Sunday Afternoon

The TV's on and the volume's loud
We're trying to beat the thundercloud.
Bedroom upstairs is a very big mess
Computer's crashed twice I have to confess
PS2's a real pain
It drives me mad this sopping rain.
Homework later, much, much later
Teacher won't mind, he's a very good waiter!

Watching DVDs highly rated
Mum gave us not popcorn, but cheese (urgh) grated!
Whilst Dad was doing some DIY
Just a cardboard tower and not very high.
My baby sister Sophie was drawing teenage Jane
She was half scribble, half stickman and to me looked very lame.
This was a boring rainy Sunday, which could have been fun
Maybe we'll be lucky next week and have a bit of sun.

Louise Taylor (9)
St Catherine's Preparatory School, Bramley

Cat

There's something furry behind that tree
Or maybe it's coming from that bee.
It could be a bear but that would scare, or it may be
Looking for its tea.

Now I'm rather scared,
I think I'll look over there,
I just hope that bear goes over there
Or runs away from me.

My voice has gone,
I hear a song,
I've found out that I was wrong,
The bear and the bee did not scare me,
I found out it was a
        Cat!

Charlotte Warner (9)
St Catherine's Preparatory School, Bramley

Cycling Through The Countryside

Cycling through the countryside,
On a warm summer's day.
It is great fun to ride
In the brilliant month of May.

Cycling through the countryside,
Through the wonderful green meadows.
I had to stop and look,
At the dormouse in the hedgerow.

Cycling through the countryside,
With the wind blowing west,
I have to try very hard,
To cycle my very best.

Cycling through the countryside,
Past me came a bee.
I smell something good,
I bet it's for my tea.

Cycling through the countryside,
As I smile with glee.
I am nearly there you know,
Guess what, I'm just in time for tea.

Georgina Rolls (10)
St Catherine's Preparatory School, Bramley

Shells

Lost and delicate, lying in the sand,
Taken then for my collector's hand.

Now in my room do they miss the sea,
Or are they happy staying with me?

Then they get washed away into the deep blue sea,
Waiting again for you and me.

Megan Burling (10)
St Catherine's Preparatory School, Bramley

The Robin

Sitting there on a branch,
With a chest so bright and red.
Looking so sad and lonely,
While I looked from my bed.

As the sun came up at dawn,
Reminding me it was nearly morn.
As he started to sing his song,
I sat and listened hard and long.

I wrapped up warm and went outside,
'I'm feeding the robin,' to my mother I cried.
He looked so lonely and cold in the snow,
I decided to stay, I just couldn't go.

And with his bright and glowing chest
For me that robin was the best.
And with his cheerful morning song,
I could sit and listen all day long.

Isabella Stevens-Harris (9)
St Catherine's Preparatory School, Bramley

Flying

Swiftly whirling through the trees
The leaves rustle in the breeze.
The bees and birds gently soaring
In the wind of the waving trees.

Fly the kite above the sky
Gently waving in the breeze.
Catch some wind and make it fly
In the wind of the waving trees.

A large balloon in the sky
Drifting far away in the breeze.
It has caught the wind to make it fly
In the wind of the waving trees.

Elizabeth Dingemans (9)
St Catherine's Preparatory School, Bramley

My Sister

My sister is called Sarah, she is twelve years old
But when I tell her what to do, she goes batty too
When I want to play with her, she shoves me away
Then I get really upset that she won't play today.
When her friends come to stay I am left alone
Then I get really jealous so I take my friends home
When I want to watch TV
She always chooses the other channel
We argue, fight and scream and then
She hits me with my flannel
Mum comes in and says, '*Stop!*'
And Sarah goes off in a strop
We then know we've gone too far
And both decide to stop the fight
With all our courage and our might
Although annoying she is my friend
And I'll love her till the very end.

Isabel Bishop (9)
St Catherine's Preparatory School, Bramley

My Love

My love, my love,
When are you going to come home?
The candles are out and there is no answer on the phone.

My love, my love
The food is cold
Although you are gone, I must be bold.

My love, my love
I can't think in my head.
I just got a call that you are dead.

My love, my love
Please watch me from above
Because you were my one, my one true love.

Courtney Madincea (10)
St Catherine's Preparatory School, Bramley

The Monster Mansion

In the monster mansion there lives,
An ambidextrous ant, doing acrobats,
A bumpy boot made of baloney,
A crazy cat that crumbles,
A droopy, dumb daddy Dracula,
An elephant eating eggs,
Frank the frankfurter,
A goat that's a Goth,
A horny hornet hopping,
An inky iguana itching,
A jammy jackal jumping,
A koala kissing a king,
A lumpy, loopy, loony, lunar lunatic,
A mangy monkey in mufti,
A naughty, numb, nipping nose,
An orange octopus organising oinkers,
A phat plump panther,
A quite quick queen quietly quacking,
A rapping rat reading,
A stupid scary snake,
A tarantula torturing troopers,
An ugly uncle's underpants uttering,
A violent vast vapour,
A wet, worthy, wagging wig,
A xylophone X-raying X-man,
A young, yucky yak,
A zooming, zany zebra,
In the monster mansion.

Abigail Vega (10)
St Catherine's Preparatory School, Bramley

The Sea In A Stew

Petrol-blue boats bucketing,
Buoys bumping,
Seagulls silent,
Driftwood drumming the foaming seashore.

Colossal mountainous waves,
Sombre night-black clouds lurking above,
Thumping sheets of rain.

Bucking and crashing,
Backwards and forwards,
Flashes of lightning,
A thunder roll,
The sea's in a stew.

Molly Standen-Jewell (10)
St Catherine's Preparatory School, Bramley

The Show

Tense, scared and excited,
Murmurs, rippling through the crowd.
Butterflies in my stomach,
Nothing else matters I have to hear 'Clear round!'

The gong has sounded,
Off we go!
Wind in my hair, pulling at my coat,
I can do this, I know.

I have done it!
But how have I done?
I patted my pony,
Who cares? At least we had fun.

Emily Wyatt (11)
St Catherine's Preparatory School, Bramley

Dolphin

It crashes through the waves,
But something catches his eye,
Down, down on the seabed,
It finds the sparkling pearl,
So delicate so serene,
Such a beauty to be seen,
Pearls for tears it misses its mother,
How long has it searched to find one another?
The net was cast, the aquarium her home,
The net took her away from her home.
The dolphin so young, all alone,
What a pity it is,
What a pity it was.

Olivia Frew (10)
St Catherine's Preparatory School, Bramley

The Armed Robber

(Inspired by 'The Highwayman' by Alfred Noyes)

The stars were a-glistening among the dark sapphire sky,
The wind was a whistling bird through the tall dark tree,
The roar of a motorbike echoed as it sped through the breeze,
And the armed robber came roaring -
     roaring - roaring
Up to the pub and hotel door.

He had a ruby-red ring on his finger,
With silver pearls on a cross,
His belt was shining in the silver moonlight,
Moss sprang up as he roared through the wind,
And he roared through the trees with a twinkle,
His jewellery was a twinkle,
His belt buckle a twinkle under the sapphire sky.

Lily German (10)
St Ives School, Haslemere

The Robber

(Inspired by 'The Highwayman' by Alfred Noyes)

The sky was a blanket of darkness over the old churchyard
The moon was a ray of sunlight standing like a guard
The road was a winding snake slithering over the moor,
And the robber came driving -
            Driving - driving
The robber came driving up to the bolted door.

He'd a gold medallion around his neck,
A tattoo on his arm,
A coat of leather and trousers as black as his charm
They fitted with no creases; his trainers up to his ankle
And he drove with a nervous sparkle
            His gun butts a-sparkle
His metal knife a sparkle under the starry sky.

Isabella Metcalfe-Smith (10)
St Ives School, Haslemere

The Mugger

(Inspired by 'The Highwayman' by Alfred Noyes)

The wind was a howling wolf among the bare cold trees.
The moon was a white pearl above the swirling leaves.
The sea was a growling dog over the outstretched moor.
And the mugger came creeping -
      Creeping - creeping
The mugger came creeping up to the old oak door.

His hair was a curly brown that ran past his ears,
He had strong muscly arms that held no fears,
He had long gold bling above a thick blue vest,
That covered his sturdy chest.

Alice Steward (9)
St Ives School, Haslemere

The Mugger

(Inspired by 'The Highwayman' by Alfred Noyes)

The rain was a shower of sorrow, among the cloudy trees
The moon was a pearl of darkness, neglected upon the seas
The street was a cord of lights, never-ending across the moor
And the mugger came a-driving -
    - driving - driving
The mugger came a-driving up to the nightclub door.

He'd a cap perched backwards on his forehead,
a lot of bling round his throat
He had tanned brown skin and wore a real leather coat
His hair was cut and styled with gel, his boots reached the knee
And he drove his bike with a glittering move
    His wheels held this glittering move.
He shot past with this glittering move, barely scraping the trees.

Georgia Frisby (10)
St Ives School, Haslemere

The Mugger

(Inspired by 'The Highwayman' by Alfred Noyes)

The wind made a ghostly whisper along the alleyway,
The moon was a staring skull, light as day.
The road was pitted with potholes, with graffiti on the walls,
And the mugger skulked closer -
    closer - closer
The mugger skulked closer, with quiet footfalls.

He'd a leather coat and a shark tooth hanging from his ear
Around his wrist he wore a watch, which shone as he came near
His crocodile boots shimmered from the moon above
His eyes had an evil twinkle,
    his knife all a-twinkle,
Money was his only love.

Meredith Leston (10)
St Ives School, Haslemere

The Hacker

(Inspired by 'The Highwayman' by Alfred Noyes)

The rain was a river of darkness among the swirling leaves,
The moon was a sullen bleary glow through the looming trees,
In the dimness of his den the computer screen glowed
As the hacker sat tapping -
    Tapping - tapping
As the hacker sat tapping the keys to the Internet road.

He'd square shaped lenses in his glasses and a mass of jagged
                                        red hair,
A jacket of denim splendour and trousers of knees torn bare,
The shimmer of nails in the moonlight and the reflective glint
                                        in his specs,
The hacker sat tapping -
    Tapping - tapping
While other lives he wrecks.

Christy Callaway-Gale (10)
St Ives School, Haslemere

The Mugger

(Inspired by'The Highwayman' by Alfred Noyes)

The lights of pubs were cats' eyes gleaming in the dark
The lights were beacons looming over Miami park.
The booming music thumped heavier as he approached the crowd,
As the mugger came riding -
    Riding - riding
The mugger came riding up to the nightclub loud.

He had a wavy mass of gelled black hair,
His chest was painted in bling,
He had a villainous tattoo placed on his hairy tanned skin,
He rode off on his motorbike
    His prize at his side on his motorbike,
His smile full of sparkly charm at his bike.

Lydia Matthews (10)
St Ives School, Haslemere

The Alcohol Robber

(Inspired by 'The Highwayman' by Alfred Noyes)

The moon was a glowing pearl among the tarmacked way,
The wind was a howling dragon shrieking at the end of day.
The sky was a sheet of darkness above the desolate moor,
And the criminal came blaring -
     Blaring - blaring
The criminal came blaring up to the old pub door.

He'd a bleeding scar on his cheek, a goatie beard on his chin,
A pair of shiny boots and round his neck some bling,
He wore his trousers baggy to match his denim coat,
And he drove with a ring on his finger,
     An expensive ring on his finger,
So many rings on his fingers,
That his heart began to gloat.

Lucy Hawkins (10)
St Ives School, Haslemere

The Mugger

(Inspired by 'The Highwayman' by Alfred Noyes)

The wind was a whistling kettle among the noiseless trees
The moon was a gleaming opal flung upon drowning seas,
The road was a river of darkness over the moonlit floor,
And the mugger came creeping -
     Creeping - creeping
The mugger came creeping up to the nightclub door.

He'd a mass of black hair to his shoulders, his chest was
Covered in bling,
A top of plain black fabric and a grotesque silver ring.
Black glasses that covered his eyes, a tattoo of a heart on his arm,
He crept with a flashing smile,
     His face lit up with a smile,
His rounded face in a smile, a smile of unspeakable charm.

Talia Morey (10)
St Ives School, Haslemere

The Drug Dealer

(Inspired by 'The Highwayman' by Alfred Noyes)

The wind was a gentle caress among the old oak trees,
The moon was a pale sea, calling back at me,
The street was lit up by clubs and pubs, everything was raw
And the drug dealer came speeding -
    Speeding - speeding
The drug dealer came speeding, up to the dirty club door.

He had long windy hair falling down over his shoulder,
And a short sleeve top, his arms getting colder.
His black loose trousers as dark as the midnight sky,
His eye did a wink, the start of a lie,
And his rings flew a twinkle
    His bling whistled a twinkle
His boots a shiny twinkle, under the dead night sky.

Katie Brooke Barnett (10)
St Ives School, Haslemere

The Mugger

(Inspired by 'The Highwayman' by Alfred Noyes)

The wind was a gust of madness among the American streets,
The rain was a spurting waterfall on top of the beggar's sheets,
The moon was the light of a lantern shining evermore,
And the mugger came driving -
    driving - driving
And the mugger came driving, towards the nightclub's door.

He'd a peaked, black cap on 'is head, an' a bling upon his chest,
A jacket of blue plastic and jeans fitting under his vest,
They fitted with not a wrinkle, his trainers hugged loosely to his feet,
And he drove with a diamond sparkle,
    His gun madly sparkled,
His bling medallion sparkled, ready for the meet.

Charlotte Ashton (9)
St Ives School, Haslemere

The Punk Rocker

(Inspired by 'The Highwayman' by Alfred Noyes)

The wind was an untuned guitar playing among the trees
The moon was a glaring limelight shining as if to please.
The street was a blanket of concrete edged with cracked cement
And the punk came driving -
       Driving - driving
The punk came driving, viciously into the night.

He had multicoloured hair that dazzled in the light,
A jumper of ruddy red that mingled giving quite a fright
They fitted with not a crinkle: his flares bagged down to the ground
He drove with a flashing menace
     His mohican hair a-menace
His toothless smile a menace in the midnight sky.

Lottie Fry (10)
St Ives School, Haslemere

The Computer Hacker

(Inspired by 'The Highwayman' by Alfred Noyes)

The wind was an angry ocean banging against the glass.
The moon a face peering upon the shimmering grass.
The road went winding down through the deserted moor,
The computer hacker came cycling -
Cycling - cycling
The computer hacker came cycling up to the library door.

The well built man had a shaven head and a dollar tattooed on his arm,
A shining ring hung from his ear, round his neck a silver charm,
His shirt was wrinkled and dirty, his shorts were down to his knees
The handle bars were shining
The wheels were slowly spinning
As he pushed his bike along the path and laid it behind the trees.

Isabella Pettit (10)
St Ives School, Haslemere

The Mugger

(Inspired by 'The Highwayman' by Alfred Noyes)

The wind was a whistling kettle
Among the silent trees,
The moon was a lighthouse beacon
Through the stormy seas,
The road was a strip of light over the high moor,
And the mugger came driving -
    Driving - driving
The mugger came driving up to the nightclub door.

He'd a cross-shaped tattoo on his arm,
Around his neck hung his bling,
A coat of real black leather, and trousers like tanned skin,
He'd a flashing smile, and a hairy chest,
And he drove with a jewelled grin.
He has a gleaming smile,
He has a big smile and it's the best part of him.

Lucy Herbert (10)
St Ives School, Haslemere

The Drug Dealer

(Inspired by 'The Highwayman' by Alfred Noyes)

The wind was a gunshot among the rough river's waves,
The trees were towering giants moving towards the rocks and caves,
The road was a path to nowhere, streams running down to the moor,
And the drug dealer came driving -
    Driving - driving
The drug dealer came driving up to the nightclub door.

He had a cap turned round on his forehead, around his neck was
His bling,
A jacket of black leather and tattoos all over his velvet skin,
He had baggy jeans down to the floor, boots up to his knees
He drove while breaking the law,

He had a gun so breaking the law,
Selling drugs was breaking the law, driving wherever he did please.

Claire Frye (10)
St Ives School, Haslemere

The Sound Collector

(Based on 'The Sound Collector' by Roger McGough)

'A stranger called this morning
Dressed all in black and grey
Put every sound into a bag
And carried them away.'

The scraping of a sharpener
The splashing of the pool
The rustling of the grass
The children shouting 'Cool!'

The bumping of a ball
The ticking of a clock
The rattle of the toast
The banging of a knock.

The crashing of the dish
The cracking of a nut
The purring of a cat
The barking of a mutt.

Matya Morey (7)
St Ives School, Haslemere

The Sound Collector

(Based on 'The Sound Collector' by Roger McGough)

The ringing of the bell
The buzzing of the light
The swishing of the fish
As the children bite.

The kettle going wild
A girl doing her zip
And another doing a backflip and
My brother doing a trick.

Ellen Hayward (7)
St Ives School, Haslemere

The Sound Collector
(Based on 'The Sound Collector' by Roger McGough)

The breathing of the girl
The panting of the boy
The girl has lost her glowing pearl
The boy has much more joy.

The swaying of the trees
The wind has made them sway
The buzzing of the bees
Then I hear children play.

The screaming of someone crying
It's a girl or a boy
She lost what she was buying
But she's got another toy.

Amy Owen (7)
St Ives School, Haslemere

The Sound Collector
(Based on 'The Sound Collector' by Roger McGough)

The flickering of the light
The wind going wild
The girl saying goodnight
To the other child.

The barking of a dog
The purring of a cat
The creaking of a log
The screeching of a bat.

The stamping of a girl
The squeaking of a mouse
The girl doing a twirl
The sounds of the house.

Sarah Baldwin (8)
St Ives School, Haslemere

The Sound Collector

(Based on 'The Sound Collector' by Roger McGough)

The speaking of a human
When they get out of bed
The loud clonking noise
When you nod and bang your head.

The pattering of some busy feet
While children run and play
The rustling in the barn
Of animals in the hay.

The ringing of the phone
When someone tries to call
The cheering in a netball match
When our team gets the ball.

Catherine Bird (7)
St Ives School, Haslemere

The Sound Collector

(Based on 'The Sound Collector' by Roger McGough)

'A stranger called this morning
Dressed all in black and grey
Put every sound into a bag
And carried them away.'

The woofing of a guard dog
The rustling of the leaves
The roaring of Concorde
The buzzing of the bees.

The squeaking of the white board
The slamming of the doors
The scratching of the pencils
Chairs scraping on the floors.

Abigail Hansford (7)
St Ives School, Haslemere

The Sound Collector

(Based on 'The Sound Collector' by Roger McGough)

The whistling of the wind
The screaming of the girl
The pumping of your heart
The plopping of an oyster's pearl.

The swaying of the sea
The bouncing of a ball
The woofing of a dog
People's feet in the hall.

The licking of a lolly
The hopping of a frog
The swaying of a tree
A very angry dog.

Jessica Clifton (8)
St Ives School, Haslemere

The Sound Collector

(Based on 'The Sound Collector' by Roger McGough)

The flickering of the light
The whistling of my mother
The smashing of a bowl
The jumping of my brother.

The noisy lot of children
The child saying I want more
The stamping of a boy
A very angry boar.

Rosie Hawkins (8)
St Ives School, Haslemere

The Sound Collector
(Based on 'The Sound Collector' by Roger McGough)

'A stranger called this morning
Dressed all in black and grey
Put every sound into a bag
And carried them away.'

The shouting of the children
The ticking of the clock
The ringing of the bell
The turning of the lock.

The stamping of the boy
The screaming of the girl
The stamping of the shoes
As she does a whirl.

Lucy Mackintosh (8)
St Ives School, Haslemere

The Sound Collector
(Based on 'The Sound Collector' by Roger McGough)

The honking of a pig
The roaring of a lion
The swishing of fish
The buzzing of an iron.

The radiator pipe
The purring of a cat
The jumping of a monkey's joy
The wiping of a mat.

The running of the mice
The humming of the birds
The drumming of a band
The racing of the herds.

Aleena Virdee (7)
St Ives School, Haslemere

Hiawatha

(Inspired by Henry Wadsworth Longfellow)

Sharp of sight was Hiawatha,
He could see an ant a blinking
He could see a mouse's teardrop
And the grains of salt within it.

Keen of ear was Hiawatha,
He could hear the mighty thunder
E'en before the lightning struck.

Loud of noise was Hiawatha
He could smite the rocks asunder
With his bold almighty voice.

He had face mask made of deerskin
When upon his face he wore it.
He could change the rainbow colours
Change the seasons of the year.

He had feathers plucked from eagles
When upon his arms he wore them
He could fly above the rain clouds
Swifter than the turtle doves.

Alexandra Herson (8)
St Ives School, Haslemere

The Sound Collector

(Based on 'The Sound Collector' by Roger McGough)

'A stranger called this morning
Dressed all in black and grey
Put every sound into a bag
And carried them away.'

The crashing of the thunder
The splashing of the rain
The banging of the door
As I scream again.

Ellie German (7)
St Ives School, Haslemere

Hiawatha

(Inspired by Henry Wadsworth Longfellow)

Sharp of sight was Hiawatha
He could see the scales of small fish
As they swam on the ocean bed
Count the scales with one eye blink
Watched as one by one they shed.

Keen of ear was Hiawatha
He could hear the sun's rays beaming
As the shadows fluttered past
They made his ears go round and round.

Loud of voice was Hiawatha
He could rattle oak bookcases
Right around the worldwide towns
With all the mighty strength he held
Made them rattle with such great power.

He had a face mask made of deerskin
When upon his face he wore it
He could make the whole world spin,
Oh such a force which made humans dizzy!

He had feathers made from eagles
When upon his arms he wore them
He could fly above the clouds
Right above the biggest rainstorm.

Emma Baker (8)
St Ives School, Haslemere

Hiawatha

(Inspired by Henry Wadsworth Longfellow)

Sharp of sight was Hiawatha
He could see each snowflake's pattern
He could see lion's mane a-growing.

Keen of ear was Hiawatha;
He could hear the silence shouting
He could hear the flowers growing.

Loud of voice was Hiawatha
He could cause an avalanche
He could make the thunder start.

He had a face mask made of feathers
When upon his face he wore it
He could dance the best around the totem pole
And become invisible.

He had feathers made from eagles
When upon his arms he wore them,
He could fly around the world
He could fly as high as the mountains.

Charlotte Taylor (8)
St Ives School, Haslemere

Hiawatha

(Inspired by Henry Wadsworth Longfellow)

Sharp of sight was Hiawatha
He would see the bottom of the ocean
Fifty fathoms deep, deep, deep.
He could stop the willow weeping
He could start a fire with nothing.

Keen of ear was Hiawatha;
He could hear the fire crackle
As it burned one mile away.
He could feel the sun a-blazing
Even though he lived on Earth.

Isabella Kirkman (8)
St Ives School, Haslemere

Hiawatha

(Inspired by Henry Wadsworth Longfellow)

Sharp of sight was Hiawatha
He could see the single crystal
Of each teardrop in the ocean
In amongst the plants and fish
He could see each single shell.

Keen of ear was Hiawatha
He could hear the bird's wing flapping
Way above the clouds and higher
He could tell where it was flying.

Loud of voice was Hiawatha
He could smite the mountain's summit
Which then landed at the bottom
Causing avalanche to happen.

He had face mask made of hard clay
When upon his face he wore it
He could change the rainbow's colours
Into hues yet brighter still.

He had feathers plucked from eagles
When upon his arms he wore them
He could fly above the mountains
Land upon the snow-capped summits.

Amelia Talfourd-Cook (8)
St Ives School, Haslemere

Hiawatha

(Inspired by Henry Wadsworth Longfellow)

Sharp of sight was Hiawatha;
He could see into the future
He could see the day at night-time
See the night at break of day.

Keen of ear was Hiawatha;
He could hear the silence shouting
He could hear the eyes a blinking.

Loud of voice was Hiawatha;
He could make the rocks slide forward
And make tomtoms play before him
Louder than a grizzly bear.

He had face mask made of feathers,
When upon his face he wore it
He could fly upon the white clouds
He could dance to change the weather.

He had feathers plucked from eagles
When upon his arms he wore them
He could fight the mighty giants
And shoot them into grains of powder.

Georgina Gulliver (8)
St Ives School, Haslemere

The Sound Collector

(Based on 'The Sound Collector' by Roger McGough)

The whistling of the wind
As I listen to the clock
The rustling of the bag
As the farmer rounds up the flock.

The kettle going wild
My sister going mad
The dustbin going bang
As my dad puts the toy in the bag.

Lauren Evans (7)
St Ives School, Haslemere

Hiawatha

(Inspired by Henry Wadsworth Longfellow)

Sharp of sight was Hiawatha
He could see into the future
He could see the sun at night-time
Beaming down on the Earth below.

Keen of ear was Hiawatha
He could hear your eyes a-blinking
He could hear your brain a-thinking
Emotions rearing up inside.

Loud of voice was Hiawatha
He could split the big tree growing,
Growing in the summer sun.

He had a face mask made of silver
When upon his face he wore it
He could turn the mud to gold
He could make the mountains mould.

He had feathers taken from eagles
When upon his arms he wore them
He could fly right up to Mars
So quickly that he beat the light.

Ellie Richards (8)
St Ives School, Haslemere

Hiawatha

(Inspired by Henry Wadsworth Longfellow)

Sharp of sight was Hiawatha;
He could see into the future
He could see the willow weeping
Count the salty, crystal grains
In the ocean oh so blue.

Keen of ear was Hiawatha;
He could hear the silence talking
He could hear his brain cogs whirring.

Loud of voice was Hiawatha;
He could smite the mighty mountains
With one word from his strong voice.

He had a face mask made of deerskin
When upon his face he wore it
Braves and squaws bowed down before him.

He had feathers plucked from eagles
When upon his arms he wore them
He could fly around the world
He flew in the opposite direction
To the Earth as it spun round
So returned to his own wigwam
E'en before his journey had begun.

Jemima Kuzemko (8)
St Ives School, Haslemere

Hiawatha

(Inspired by Henry Wadsworth Longfellow)

Sharp of sight was Hiawatha
He could see the teeth of beetle
Watch the teardrop fall from a small fly
Soon as it had left the eye.

Keen of ear was Hiawatha
He could hear the daisies shouting
Shouting with such power and uproar
E'er the wind had blown their voices.

Loud of voice was Hiawatha
He could smite the trees asunder
With a cry from the mountain tops
He could split the grass with whisper.

He had face mask made of buckskin
When upon his face he wore it,
He could live in elders' bodies
With their spirits camouflaged.

He had feathers made from ravens
When upon his arms he wore them,
Invisible he made himself
Spying on the big world dangers.

Georgina Wedge (8)
St Ives School, Haslemere

Hiawatha

(Inspired by Henry Wadsworth Longfellow)

Sharp of sight was Hiawatha
He could see the mouse's teardrop
See the salt on mouse's cheek
As the droplets fell from eye.

Keen of ear was Hiawatha
He could hear your hair a-growing
Hear the many brain cogs ticking
E'er he knew what you were thinking.

Loud of voice was Hiawatha
He could crack a big volcano,
He could stop the lava flowing
Start an earthquake miles away.

He had face mask made of feathers
When upon his face he wore it,
He could fly above the sky
Scatter birds from far away.

He had feathers taken from phoenix
When upon his arms he wore them,
He could draw birds from their nests
Attracted from distance far.

Olivia Dower-Tylee (9)
St Ives School, Haslemere

Hiawatha

(Inspired by Henry Wadsworth Longfellow)

Sharp of sight was Hiawatha
He could see a cold wind blowing
He could make his enemies go away.

Keen of ear was Hiawatha
He could hear the conversations
Of every person in the world.

Loud of voice was Hiawatha
He could push a snow capped mountain
Just by yelling 'Go!' and shouting.

He had a face mask made of leather
When upon his face he wore it
He could scare the mighty dragons
He could do the best rain dance.

He had feathers made from eagles
When upon his arms he wore them
He could smash a great volcano.

Phoebe Smith (8)
St Ives School, Haslemere

The Drug Dealer

(Inspired by 'The Highwayman' by Alfred Noyes)

The moon was a shining opal shimmering in the dull seas
The wind was a forceful dragon dodging between the trees
The road was a ribbon of darkness full of grief and gore
And the drug dealer came driving -
    Driving - driving
The drug dealer came driving up to the nightclub door.

He'd a full length coat on his shoulders, a couple of E in his pocket
His vest was full of holes and his wide eyes gleamed in their sockets
His suit hung loosely with plenty of room to spare
And he drove with a boom of music
      His loud, loud booming music
His car was full of music under the threatening air.

Lucy Jenner (9)
St Ives School, Haslemere

Hiawatha

(Inspired by Henry Wadsworth Longfellow)

Sharp of sight was Hiawatha
He could see the sun at night-time
He could see the moon at daytime
See the planets and bright, bright stars.

Keen of ear was Hiawatha
He could hear the distant brook
Rushing downstream miles onwards
Heading for the giant ocean.

Loud of voice was Hiawatha
He could make the mountains crumble
Grind them into finest powder
See the mountains miserable.

He had a face mask made of feathers
When upon his face he wore it
He could turn to a buffalo
Turn into a small sparrow.

He had feathers plucked from Griffin
When upon his head he wore them
He could melt the freezing snow
He could stop the north wind blow.

Amelia Frase (8)
St Ives School, Haslemere

Hiawatha

(Inspired by Henry Wadsworth Longfellow)

Sharp of sight was Hiawatha
Sees the toenails of a red ant
Trims them with his tomahawk.

Keen of ear was Hiawatha
He could hear the butterflies
Flapping round the candlelight
Hear the noise of bluebirds singing
Hear its feather floating downwards.

Loud of voice was Hiawatha
He could turn day into night-time
With one scream and two long howls.

He had a face mask made of silver
When upon his face he wore it,
He could smite the tallest mountain,
He could dance the fastest dance.

He had feathers taken from a peacock
When upon his arms he wore them,
He could fly as high as birds
Each day make a new disguise.

Eve Franklin (8)
St Ives School, Haslemere

Hiawatha

(Inspired by Henry Wadsworth Longfellow)

Sharp of sight was Hiawatha
He could see the willow weeping
He could make the willow smile.

Keen of ear was Hiawatha
He could hear the moon a-snoring
When he put his head to the ground
He could hear the worms below.

Loud of voice was Hiawatha
He could cause an avalanche
Just by singing at the powwow
While dancing round the totem pole.

He had a face mask made from beavers
When upon his face he wore it
He could kill a big brown bear
He could see into the future
Know when the enemy was there.

He had feathers made from wild hawks,
When upon his arms he wore them,
He could hunt the roaming wild deer
Kill a hundred with one spear.

Holly Barcham (8)
St Ives School, Haslemere

My Favourite Rhyme

The rhyme is about an actor,
Comedian from the past,
Had a strange walk of his own,
And a funny moustache.

He comes back to the future,
Playing golf with his stick,
He whacks at a potato,
But then he loses it.

A small boy comes to the rescue
With a hot potato fast,
He tried it again
But didn't win,
And that was the end of the past.

Bobbie Hook (10)
St Ives School, Haslemere

Boat Kennings

Large floater
Smoke belcher
People carrier
Water speeder
Rack leader.

Lawrence Swithinbank (10)
St Martin's CE Primary School, Dorking

Me

Sport sprinter
Friend maker.

Spaghetti slurper,
Sweet stuffer.

Cat cuddler,
Teddy hugger.

Veggie hater,
Book loser.

TV watcher,
Music lover.

Computer crazy,
Dancing diva.

That's just me!

Eleanor Carroll (10)
St Martin's CE Primary School, Dorking

Wolves

Wolves are hairy
Wolves are smooth
Wolves are always on the move
There are big ones
There are small ones
But they travel in tonnes
Wolves are fat
Wolves are thin
And they eat out of the bin
They are always admired
At the end of the day, they are tired.

Alexander Jackson (9)
St Martin's CE Primary School, Dorking

The Red Riding Rap

There was a girl called
Little Miss Red
Whose Granny was sick
And tucked up in bed.
She saw some flowers to pick
And ran to her granny's, quick, quick, quick.
A big bad wolf heard her plan
The big bad wolf he ran, ran, ran.
He got into Granny's through the door
Locked her in the cupboard with a great big roar.
He took her place in the bed
And pulled the nightie over his head.
He waited for little Miss to come in
Then the big bad wolf would have his din.
Little Miss came in, he had his din
And chucked old Granny in the bin.
The woodcutter saw the bad wolf's jaw
Got out his axe and came through the door.
He cut the wolf up
And with a hiccup he coughed her up
And that's the end of my rap!

Chris Mahony (9)
St Martin's CE Primary School, Dorking

The Moon

The moon is like a silver pool
Sparkling, shimmering, beautiful.

The moon is like a giant ring
So big but looks so small.

The moon is a changing sphere
Never falling from the sky.

Megan Davey (9)
St Martin's CE Primary School, Dorking

Skiing In The Sun

Skiing is very scary
But makes me feel so wary.

It's fun in the sun
Going down the slopes
With my hopes
Of not falling then bawling.

I seek the mountain peaks
To get my thrills and see the hills.

The snow is cold but bold
But I don't care I still will dare.

I take the challenge from the top
And slide down with a flop.

It's all good fun doing these runs.

The end of day is near
No more falling on my rear.

My one thought is that I ought
to get back up and start again
another day, another way.

Yasmin Baker (10)
St Martin's CE Primary School, Dorking

I Have . . .

I have lived and I have died
I have swum in the sea
I have loved and I have hated
I have walked on land
I have spoken the word
I have heard the unspoken word
I have seen the life of an angel.

Nadia Correa Gomez (9)
St Martin's CE Primary School, Dorking

A Little Sister

Heavy sleeper
Eats pizza.

Cries a lot
Wees in a pot.

Loves teddies
Hates Shreddies.

Ginger hair
But doesn't care.

Cute clothes
Can't resist a pose.

Heavy drinker
Big stinker.

Messy eater
Terrible speaker.

Likes Sundays
Hates Mondays.

Constant weeper
Heavy sleeper.

Hannah Perrin (9)
St Martin's CE Primary School, Dorking

Books

Books can be big
Books can be small
Books can be silly
We love them all.

Books can be paperback
Books can be hard
Books can be about anything
Or they can be made out of card.

Lucy Holden (9)
St Martin's CE Primary School, Dorking

Brother

Biscuit muncher
Big puncher
Bogey flicker
Big ogre
Bog hogger
Some snogger
Tough growler
Big howler
Makes mad
Mum, Dad
Comes home
Heats up Dad.

Rachel Gregson (10)
St Martin's CE Primary School, Dorking

Dad

Smelly smoker
My joker
Super soaker
Nappy no-er
Lawn mower
Bad sewer
Bad knitter
Super sitter
Bad footer
Loo lover
He's my dad.

Ben Hardman (9)
St Martin's CE Primary School, Dorking

Sing A Song Of Sixty Pence

Sing a song of sixty pence
An apple that is red
A bunch of ripe bananas
More eating and less said
Queue up for your healthy food
More delicious pear
It's food like this in superstores
That makes you stop and stare.

Dinah Rodell (10)
St Martin's CE Primary School, Dorking

Winter

Snowdrops fall to the ground
Children run all around
Snowballing
Snowflakes falling
Sledges gliding
Animals hiding
Winds are blowing
Rivers stop flowing.

Rosanna Stech (9)
St Martin's CE Primary School, Dorking

Autumn

Leaves are falling, winter's calling
Children run, they scream and shout
Leaves are orange, yellow and brown
They are tumbling and shooting down
Piles of leaves, a cool breeze.

Emily O'Brien (10)
St Martin's CE Primary School, Dorking

Chartwell

Once we went to Chartwell
I thought it was really cool.

There is the kitchen
And there is the hall.

Plus don't forget the swimming pool
And the concrete wall.

Churchill saved the whole wide world
With Britain helping as well.

Germany fell down that hole
While Britain stood up tall.

Zoe Nash (10)
St Martin's CE Primary School, Dorking

Cinquain

The match
I'm on the pitch
'Go Brazil, good shot, *goal!*'
3-1, We won! Goalkeeper had
No chance.

Fergus Harding (9)
St Martin's CE Primary School, Dorking

Grandpa

Lazy sleeper
Granny peeper
Gardening craze
In a daze
Early mornings
Always yawning
Feeding birds
Making apple curds
Going grey
Not fit to play

That's my grandpa
He's my superstar!

Elsa Hartley (9)
St Martin's CE Primary School, Dorking

A Field Mouse

A field mouse runs through the wheat,
Ready to greet
His friends with pattering feet,
Coming from the bright hot heat.
They all love to eat
The wheat,
So sweet.

Sarah Watson (9)
St Martin's CE Primary School, Dorking

A Cheeky Little Monster

School hater
Dirt lover
Unhealthy eater
Slime monster
Sleeping hater
Chocolate gobbler
A cheeky
Little monster.

Alex Fyffe (9)
St Martin's CE Primary School, Dorking

Rainbow

Rainbows come
Rainbows go
Or maybe they just glitter and glow.

In the summer they reappear
And then disappear
Sometimes they're bright
But then they go out at night!

Meg Loftus (10)
St Martin's CE Primary School, Dorking

Cat

Mouse killer
Bed sleeper
Food filler
Grim creeper
Wall climber
Bird catcher
Milk lapper
Rat rhymer.

Ben Bessant (9)
St Martin's CE Primary School, Dorking

Friendship

Friendship is here
Friendship is there
Friendship is everywhere

Is hope
Is love

It makes me tingly
It makes me happy
It makes me lucky

It is kind
It is floating.

It is in your heart
It is in your blood.

Friendship is magical
Friendship is wonderful.

Chloe Veale (8)
St Peter's CE (Aided) Primary School, Wrecclesham

One Day I Lost My Hamster

One day I lost my hamster
I don't know where it went,
He could be in a tent,
Or he could have gone to Kent.

I don't know where he has gone
He could be in a stack of hay
He could have gone to play,
I wish that he would stay.

He might be in a rocket
Blasting off to space
He might be in a strange place
I miss his furry face.

Jonathan Burns (9)
St Peter's CE (Aided) Primary School, Wrecclesham

The Forest Watcher

'Who flies over the forest?'
said the blackbird . . . 'I
Fly over the fresh green trees,
And dive through the branches and out
into the sky.'

'Who will slither in the forest?'
said the snake . . . 'I
Will weave in and out of the bushes,
And crawl up the forest trees!'

'Who will keep watch of the forest?'
said the squirrel . . . 'I
Will run up the trees,
And sit on the top leaves.'

Chloe Dibnah (9)
St Peter's CE (Aided) Primary School, Wrecclesham

Can't Wait

Can't wait to be eight
Can't wait to get a mobile phone.
Can't wait to be eight
Can't wait to get new clothes.
Can't wait to be eight
Can't wait to get high-heeled shoes.
Can't wait to be *eight!*

Samantha Rogers (8)
St Peter's CE (Aided) Primary School, Wrecclesham

The Child Spirit

A small girl at the age of five goes in search of a beehive.

That's a child's spirit.

A small girl with her teddy goes out and gets all muddy.

That's a child's spirit.

A small boy adventurous and strong goes out running for very long.

That's a child's spirit.

A small girl, trendy and fashionable dresses in grown-up clothes
and make-up.

That's not a child's spirit.

We have got to keep our magic then we can go ecstatic.

That's children's spirit!

Martha Teverson (9)
St Peter's CE (Aided) Primary School, Wrecclesham

Hope

Hope is the colour of a clear blue sky.
Hope smells like lavender that has just been sprinkled
over a grassy meadow.
Hope tastes like freshly baked bread.
Hope sounds like birds singing sweetly in the distance.
Hope lives in a lap of a homeless beggar
somewhere in the streets of London.

Sophie Gale (10)
St Peter's CE (Aided) Primary School, Wrecclesham

The Smuggler

It was a dark and misty night the moon was hidden by clouds
The smuggler came down from the hill
He was dressed in black with a sack upon his back and pistols
in his belt
Clip-clop went his horses' hooves as he rode through the
dusty dirty street.
Some people spotted him and wondered who he was
But one person recognised the smuggler and got the police.
They had a bloody battle but the police came out on top
And if it's a dark and misty night in the town you can still hear
their gunshots in the dusty dirty street.

Tom Graham (9)
St Peter's CE (Aided) Primary School, Wrecclesham

Hope

Hope is the colour of a cornfield
at its ripest,
Hope smells like freshly cooked bread
and hope tastes like your
favourite pudding.
Hope sounds like birds tweeting
on Midsummer's day,
Though hope lives on the
fluffiest cloud.

Jonathan Wright (10)
St Peter's CE (Aided) Primary School, Wrecclesham

Madness In The Zoo

All the tigers chasing the monkeys
All the elephants squirting their trunkeys.

All the snakes hissing here and there,
All the guests couldn't stare.

All the giraffes eating leaves,
All the zookeepers paying fees.

All the elephants sucking up water from the water fountains
All the deer climbing mountains.

All the guests being sick
All the zookeepers getting buckets quick.

All the animals being put in their cage
After that there was no rage.

Joseph Tindall (9)
St Peter's CE (Aided) Primary School, Wrecclesham

The Smugglers

In the middle of the night it is dark and gloomy
And you hear a sudden bang, bang high up under the floorboards
You dare look out of your window, can you hear the damp, cool
wind whistling and whirling round you?
They're creeping into your house, they're standing round you.
Outside is a long dark figure crawling around, the small, stumbled
Horses gallop across the highlands, the black riders disappear at
The break of dawn and now left
Is the black rider's cloak.

Shelley MacLachlan (10)
St Peter's CE (Aided) Primary School, Wrecclesham

The Black Rider

Who is this man, he rides on his horse
back, through the tall green trees?
If you hear his galloping black stallion with a
bluster of wind, stay extremely still.

You won't like what he can do, the huge white moon shining
bright making a great deal of light on that old open road,
mist and gloom is lurking around the moon sailing across a
sheet of black blazing jewels in the sky above a town in the
middle of nowhere.

The old man had a brown-haired daughter
a beautiful daughter the one the Black Rider longed to be with,
he said, 'My love, leave this place with me across the meadows
through the wide oceans, live a life being rich, I'll gallop back
with a pile of gold before dawn.'
The lovely daughter tied a silver love knot into her hair gleaming
like the sun.
King Henry's men marched on the road.
The Rider's love fired a gold pistol out the see-through window
warning her rider not to come back.

Henry sprinted up the stairs and wielded the sword into her throat.
Suddenly a loud bang covered the air
and the Rider was as dead as a doornail.

His scimitar on the open road, if you see him on his steed
on the hillside with his haunting face and frightening breath just
remember the tale of the Black Rider.

Mason Redman (9)
St Peter's CE (Aided) Primary School, Wrecclesham

A Smugglers' Night

In the hours of darkness when it is dark,
And the candles are fluttering in the cool damp wind,
You can hear the clip-clop of hooves,
It's a smugglers' night.

Listening to the current of air in the trees,
And the smugglers' voices tittering,
It's a smugglers' night.

In the dark you can hear the shuffle of money,
The men snigger and snuffle,
In the moonless night the horses' huffs and huds,
It's a smugglers' night.

On the highway he rides, through the ribboned road,
He rides to the horizon and is never seen again,
That's a smugglers' night.

Charlie Trenholm (10)
St Peter's CE (Aided) Primary School, Wrecclesham

Tiger Began

Tiger began
She stole the orange from the blazing fire,
She stole the blackness of the burning coals
And made her coat.

Tiger began
She stole the shine of a gleaming gold coin,
She stole the blackness of a dog's wet nose
And made her eyes.

Tiger began
She stole the swiftness of an eagle
She stole the speed of Concorde
And made her run.

Sarah Day (10)
St Peter's CE (Aided) Primary School, Wrecclesham

Pig Began

Pig began.
He used the roughness of the bark,
He used the colour of the flamingo,
And made his skin.
He used the bounciness of a spring,
He used a curl of permed hair,
And made his tail.
He used the roundness of a button,
He used the strength of a shovel,
And made his nose.
He used the shape of a pea,
He used the colour of shiny coal,
And made his eyes.
He used the size of dogs' ears,
He used the floppiness of petals,
And made his ears.
Pig was made.

Sally Paine (10)
St Peter's CE (Aided) Primary School, Wrecclesham

Tiger Began

Tiger began
He grabbed the blackness of the coal
He grabbed the unevenness of a shell
And made his stripes.

For his hunt
He grabbed the slyness of a fox
He grabbed the quietness of an owl,
He grabbed the swiftness of water.

From the deep of the jungle
He grabbed the thinness of the leaves
He grabbed the whiteness of the clouds
For his whiskers.

Elissa Blankley (10)
St Peter's CE (Aided) Primary School, Wrecclesham

Tiger Began

Tiger began
He used the whiteness of the moon,
He used the colour of the peach,
He used the darkness of the night,
He used the softness of the snow,
And made his coat.

For his whiskers
He used the thinnest of the string,
He used the whiteness of the polar bear,
He used the strength of the wire.

He used the sharpness of the new knife,
He used the pointiness of the pencil,
He used the strength of the metal
For his teeth.

And tiger was completed.

Charlotte Gregory (10)
St Peter's CE (Aided) Primary School, Wrecclesham

Tiger Began

To make his fur,
He stole the softness of a new woolly jumper,
He pinched the orangeness of a blazing fire,
He stole the blackness of a starless night
And his coat was completed.

He stole the sharpness of a used dagger,
He pinched the glisten of a drooping icicle,
He stole the strength of a sledgehammer,
And finally his teeth were made.

He pinched the point of a sharpened pencil,
He grabbed the straightness of starch,
He grabbed the whiteness of a sparkly snowflake,
And finally his whiskers were made.

Jamie Crawford (10)
St Peter's CE (Aided) Primary School, Wrecclesham

Tiger Began

Tiger began,
He pinched the orange from the blazing, setting sun,
He pinched white from the frosty snow,
He pinched the jet-black from the charging snowball
And created his coat.

For his hunting
He stole the stealth of a swooping barn owl,
He stole the silence of a squealing squirrel
And made his hunting.

For his fighting
He borrowed the power of a giant sumo wrestler,
He borrowed the grip of an F1 car tyre
And made his fighting.

Luke Usher (10)
St Peter's CE (Aided) Primary School, Wrecclesham

African Animals

I went to the zoo
I found a leopard in a tree, which talked to me
Then he roared, 'Go away' to me.

I went to the zoo
I found a monkey
Eating bananas
Then he threw the peel at me.

I went to the zoo
I found a seal splashing in the pool
I got soaking wet
So I had to go home!

Ryan Gregory (8)
St Peter's CE (Aided) Primary School, Wrecclesham

Tiger Began

Tiger began
He borrowed the silk from a butterfly cocoon
He borrowed the glow of a ghost
And made his whiskers.

For his stripes
He borrowed the blackness of a pupil
He borrowed the zigzag of lightning
He borrowed the softness of smooth sand,
And his stripes were made.

For his ears
He borrowed the point of the pencil
He borrowed the alertness of a sheepdog
He borrowed the wriggle out of the worms
And his ears were made.

For his teeth
He borrowed the shine from ice glittering
He borrowed the sharpness of an axe
He borrowed the chewing of a llama
And his teeth were made.

Helen Stewart (10)
St Peter's CE (Aided) Primary School, Wrecclesham

African Animal

A rhino is grey
A rhino is fast
A rhino is strong
A rhino is big
A rhino is fat
A rhino has big tusks
A rhino has lots of teeth
A rhino loves to swim.

Macauleigh Steel (8)
St Peter's CE (Aided) Primary School, Wrecclesham

Tiger Began

Tiger began
He took the sharpness of a silver sword,
He took the strength of metal,
And made his teeth.

For his coat,
He took the softness of wool,
He took the stripes of a zebra,
He took the thickness of a woolly jumper,
And made his coat.

For his hunt,
He took the silence of a stone,
He took the speed of sound,
And he could hunt.

For his whiskers
He took the white of snow
He took the softness of human hair,
He took the sharpness of ice,
And made his whiskers,
And tiger was made.

Matthew Bolton (9)
St Peter's CE (Aided) Primary School, Wrecclesham

Friendship

Friendship is like love,
Take care of it,
Don't make friendship unhappiness,
Make it happiness,
Don't break happiness or friendship or love.

Friendship is precious,
Friendship is kind,
Friendship is care,
Friendship is loving, it tells the truth,
Friendship is a heart,
I love it!

Georgia Binfield (7)
St Peter's CE (Aided) Primary School, Wrecclesham

Tiger Began

Tiger began
He stole the reflection of a burning flame
He stole the shine of the clear moon
His eyes were complete.

He seized the firmness of the rigid granite
He seized the white of winter
He seized the jagged edges of broken glass
His teeth were made.

To create his roar
He reached for the noise of a wild rock concert
He reached for the gruff noise of an old man
He reached for the roar of a Formula 1 car.

To make his coat
He grabbed the orange of the setting sun
He grabbed the softness of a sheepskin blanket
Tiger was formed.

Susan Wright (10)
St Peter's CE (Aided) Primary School, Wrecclesham

Friendship

Friendship is precious
Friendship is kind
Friendship is love
Friendship is good.

Friendship feels nice
Friendship feels good
Friendship feels kind
Friendship feels precious.

Friendship has good in it
Friendship has love in it
Friendship has friendship in it
That's what I think.

Erin Beesley (7)
St Peter's CE (Aided) Primary School, Wrecclesham

Tiger Began

To make his fur
He stole the softness of a new woolly jumper
He pinched the orangeness of a blazing fire
He stole the blackness of a starless night
And his coat was completed.

He stole the sharpness of a used dagger
He pinched the glisten of a drooping icicle
He stole the strength of a sledgehammer
And finally his teeth were finished.

He pinched the point of a sharpened pencil
He stole the straightness of starch
He pinched the whiteness of a sparkly snowflake
And finally his whiskers were made.

Finally the tiger was created.

Rebecca Cooles (9)
St Peter's CE (Aided) Primary School, Wrecclesham

African Animals

The thump of an elephant, thump, thump, thump,
The stampede of a warthog, thump, thump, thump,
The chomp of a lion's jaw, chomp, chomp, chomp,
The chomp of an alligator, chomp, chomp, chomp,
The stretch of a giraffe, stretch, stretch, stretch,
The stretch of a leopard, stretch, stretch, stretch,
The giggle of a hyena, giggle, giggle, giggle,
The giggle of a human child, giggle, giggle, giggle

And most of all
The whisper of God
Whisper, whisper, whisper.

Claire Bolton (7)
St Peter's CE (Aided) Primary School, Wrecclesham

Tiger Began

Tiger began
She hunted the sharpness of a carving knife,
She hunted the point of a needle
And her teeth were made.

She hunted the blackness of the night,
She hunted the flames of fire,
She hunted the softness of velvet,
To make her coat.

For her eyes,
She hunted the depth of a bottomless well,
She hunted the glare of luminous car lights,
She hunted the gleam of an emerald.

She hunted the broken voice of an old man,
She hunted the snarl of a wolf on a midnight prowl,
She hunted the creaking voice of an old chair,
And made her voice,
At last she was created.

Georgia Cunningham (11)
St Peter's CE (Aided) Primary School, Wrecclesham

If I Could Be A Cheetah

Cheetahs are fast
Cheetahs have spots all over their bodies
Cheetahs are a sort of cat
        Cheetahs are fast.
Never go near a cheetah,
Never touch a cheetah
        (Warning) Cheetahs are meat-eaters.
I will not go near a cheetah
I will not touch a cheetah,
A cheetah might eat a teacher!

Benjamin Stewart (7)
St Peter's CE (Aided) Primary School, Wrecclesham

Tiger Began

He copied the stripes of the zebra,
He pinched the orange glow of the sun,
He stole the soft touch of the spider's silk,
And made his coat.

He took the quick legs of the cheetah
He took the speed of the wind,
He walked away with the stiff silence of walls,
And made his run.

He reeled in the swiftness of the snake,
He robbed the spring of a bungee,
He borrowed the silent stealth of the SAS
And made his hunt.

He robbed the range of the radar,
He stole the sharp look of a hawk
He took the glowing green of the grass
And made his eyes.

Tiger was created.

Alastair Viner (11) & Steven Simpson (10)
St Peter's CE (Aided) Primary School, Wrecclesham

I Have Friendship

I have friendship in my heart,
It really makes me feel a start.
Friendship is not that you don't care,
Or else you won't have anything to spare.
I have a friend and you do too,
Or you won't have anything to do.

My best friend is right by me,
Do you know her?
Find out and you'll see.

Kirsty MacLachlan (7)
St Peter's CE (Aided) Primary School, Wrecclesham

The Rhino

Rhinos jump around,
Rhinos buttt animals,
They eat thorns and leaves,
They destroy anything in their way,
If you met one you might freeze in your tracks,
If you run the rhino catches you easily,
So never go near a rhino,
And remember God made lots of things.

Riley Desmond (7)
St Peter's CE (Aided) Primary School, Wrecclesham

Friendship

Friendship is about love, caring and happiness,
It is good to have friendship,
Without friendship there would not be any fun,
So you must have friends,
Friendship is the purpose of the world.

Tommy Marshall (7)
St Peter's CE (Aided) Primary School, Wrecclesham

Friendship

Friendship is love,
Friendship is kind,
Friendship is special,
Friendship is important.

Friendship is good
Friendship is precious
Friendship is God
Friendship is respect.

Friendship is honesty
Friendship is hope.

I will never . . .
Never break it.

Laila Khan (7)
St Peter's CE (Aided) Primary School, Wrecclesham

Friendship

Friendship is important
Friendship is love
Friendship is kind
Friendship is love in our heart
Friendship is special.

Friendship has kindness in it
Friendship is friendship and it will not be broken
Between your friends.
Friendship has got love in it.
Friendship has caring in it.

Friendship is life,
Friendship is in your blood.
Take care of it.

Leah Puttick (7)
St Peter's CE (Aided) Primary School, Wrecclesham

Love

Love is special
Don't let it tear you apart
Let it soothe inside your body
Don't let it burn up
To meet the hissing of the dark
That can bellow in your heart
Let love help you be as ripe as a berry
In the bliss of the bright morning sun
In the tune of the birds
Will let a miner dig through the loving
Twinkling spring garden
Never let go
So let it shine above you
Let yourself go
Let love lift you from the ground
And fall like a bluebird
Tapping out the rhythm of love
Love shall forgive you (if you do wrong)
Love is our father.

Kirsty Wright (7)
St Peter's CE (Aided) Primary School, Wrecclesham

Wildlife!

In the distance
I can see a leopard leaping on the hill.
In a field
I can smell the lavender that's purple,
I can touch soft green grass
Swaying to and fro
All around me I can see
Everything lovely like wildlife and plants.

Henry Royan (8)
St Peter's CE (Aided) Primary School, Wrecclesham

Friendship

Never break it,
Never drop it,
Never throw it away,
Never put it in the fire,
Always keep it at least for one day.

Friendship of course I won't throw it away,
I shall keep it at least for one day.

I will . . .
Never break it
Never drop it
Never throw it away,
I will keep it for more than one day.

Hannah Hillyer (8)
St Peter's CE (Aided) Primary School, Wrecclesham

Love

Love is friendship
Love is my friend
And if there wasn't love
I would be sad.
Look at love.
Yes it is love.
It's love.
In my heart.

Emma Barratt (7)
St Peter's CE (Aided) Primary School, Wrecclesham

A Baby Is A Gift Of . . .

A baby is a gift from God . . .
It brings happiness and a joyful life,
Delicate and innocent like a rose.

A baby is a gift of love . . .
Cute and cuddly like a baby bear,
Soft, kind-hearted, pure and clean like angels.

A baby is a gift of joy . . .
Wins hearts by giving a beautiful smile,
That makes anyone's day full of happy joy.

A baby is a gift of life . . .
Brings a special kind of love into our lives,
What a wonderful new world lies ahead,
Lives are never the same!

Ghazia Ahmed (10)
Sandfield CP School

My Favourite Football Team

Football is great, it's really great,
but there's one thing I tell you, I really hate.
It is when my team, my favourite team,
Slip and slide all over the scene.
I get angry, I get sad, I get really, really mad.
My friends make fun and tease, I think,
. . . I've got the football loser's disease.

But when they win and do their best,
My head's in a spin and then I rest.
I think about the match I've seen,
I think about the way they've been.
My team has won, they're top of the league
And that is really all I need
From my favourite football team.

Jeremy Greenwood (9)
Sandfield CP School

An Adventure In Space

Come closer, come closer,
I'll tell you something I know.
It happened tomorrow, and it gives me a glow.

I was inside just then,
Starting to bake,
When a crash shook the Earth, and the batter of my cake.

I went outside,
And there I saw,
A tiny little spaceship, standing low.

Next came the aliens,
They invited me in,
When I got inside, I felt like a pin.

We travelled far,
We travelled wide,
We got to Planet X and we met our guide.

I recognised him
As soon as I stepped out,
For he was none other than mad Professor Clout.

The aliens disappeared,
And so did the spaceship,
When I turned round to see them, I gave an almighty flip.

Old Professor Clout smiled,
And informed me,
That to return home safely, I'd have to pay a small fee.

I worked all day,
And I worked all night,
Of course I had to give in without a fight.

Finally at last,
The craft was ready,
I fell asleep inside, back in my kitchen safe and steady.

Govindi Deerasinghe (9)
Sandfield CP School

Pie In The Sky

There's a pie in the sky and I don't know why I couldn't reach it,
it was too high.
I couldn't reach it on a dog, I couldn't reach it on a log.

There's a pie in the sky and I don't know why,
I couldn't reach it, it was too high.
I couldn't reach it on a plough, I couldn't reach it on a cow.

There's a pie in the sky and I don't know why,
I couldn't reach it, it was too high.
I couldn't reach it on a hill,
I couldn't reach it on a mill.

There's a pie in the sky and I don't know why,
I couldn't reach it, it was too high.
I couldn't reach it on a fountain,
I couldn't reach it on a mountain.

There's a pie in the sky and I don't know why,
I couldn't reach it, it was too high.
I couldn't reach it on a guy who could hover,
Now I really don't give a bother.

Tal Parmenter (10)
Sandfield CP School

Sweets

Chocolate, chocolate all around,
Starts from the ceiling down to the ground.
Full of cocoa, sugar and cream,
I think it would be every child's dream.
Chocolate, bonbons, pastilles, sweets,
It would be everyone's best treat.
Sticky, chewy, rots your teeth
Or would you much prefer to eat a leaf?
Colourful wrappers tempting you,
Silver, gold, orange and blue,
Ready to be eaten, sitting on the shelf.
I will buy them and gobble them up myself.

Jake Harris (9)
Sandfield CP School

???

Can you guess what day it is?
Well I got a shooting PS2 game,
I got a bar of my fab chocolate and
My twin brother got the same.
I got a remote control car with lots of gears on,
I got an amazing game called 'Pass the Bomb,'
I got a super games console,
And one of those games where you have to hit
The rabbits before they go down the hole.
Ahhh! I am so excited, it's my party tomorrow,
Yes you have guessed, it's my birthday,
Now I am a big six-year-old boy.

I'm not five anymore,
I can even reach the handle of the front and back doors,
People won't think of me as a baby now,
I can do my own things somehow.
Maybe now I can stay up late,
Even to quarter to eight.

Next year I will be seven
Hay same age as my best friend Kevin!

Sarah Millyard (10)
Sandfield CP School

There Was A Young Girl From Khyber

There was a young girl from Khyber,
Who sat on a stripy red tiger,
He bit off her hand
She said, *'Oh that's grand!'*
I wouldn't sit on him either.

Paige Donnithorne (9)
Sandfield CP School

Favourite Foods

Favourite food,
Favourite food,
These are a few of my favourite foods.

There's donuts and cronuts!
Things that I've never even heard of!
There's cheese before bedtime,
There's lemon and lime,
There's cream on my strawberries,
There's cream on my cherries,
Ooh I'm feeling hungry,
Am I having a dream?

There's pizza and hot dogs,
And also those gorgeous chocolate logs!
Mmm what else is there?
Oh yeah,
Hula Hoops and Haribo loops
Well that's about it really,
Those were my favourite foods!

Nicole Stracey (9)
Sandfield CP School

Chocolate

Chocolate, chocolate is the best
Chocolate, chocolate beats the rest
Chocolate, chocolate I've got nothing more to say
Apart from the fact that I want it every day.

Vedika Savania (9)
Sandfield CP School

The Battle Of Four Puddings

The reason for the battle
Was four delicious puddings,
It was fought by four armies,
Obeying four greedy boys.

As the armies kept on marching
They started to feel less grand,
Their shields of jelly started
Flopping in the sand.

Until at last they met,
At the battleground,
They stared at each other for a while,
And no one made a sound.

Suddenly the silence was broken
By a soldier from one side's team,
'Shouldn't we be fighting?' he cried,
'As strange as it may seem!'

'What a good idea,' said another
'I would have never thought of that!'
The first custard bomb was launched
And it landed with a splat!

Then one small man came down,
From the tree he'd been hiding in,
He scoffed the puddings there and then,
The battle had been won!

Connor Stanton (11)
Sandfield CP School

Space

Rattling through space,
Passing planets and stars,
You swerve past a satellite,
And ahead of you is Mars!

It's like a dream come true,
In fact it's like a movie,
Except you're not a superstar,
And you're definitely not groovy!

In space it's a completely different world,
All you can do is float,
The food is really boring and plain,
And you can't wear an ordinary coat!

So a trip to the stars could be awesome,
For travelling at the speed of sound,
But thinking about the choice of food,
I'd rather be here on the ground!

James Colinese (11)
Sandfield CP School

Pizza

Pizza here, pizza there,
Pizza, pizza everywhere
Pizza trees, a pizza house,
A pizza cat chasing a pizza mouse.
Pizza people eating pizza pies
Underneath their pizza skies.

Ben Stone (9)
Sandfield CP School

Homework, Oh Homework

Sitting at my table,
Bored out of my face,
Oh how I wish I was
In some other place.

Been to school for hours
Finally I get home
'Get and do your homework,'
Mum says with a moan.

So sitting at my table
Bored out of my face
Have to get it done,
So I can have some fun.

Tara Burton (9)
Sandfield CP School

The Summer Is Going To Bed

The autumn leaves begin to fall,
Orange and brown and red,
The day begins to get quite cool,
The summer is going to bed.

The birds fly south to warmer countries,
The cattle are in the shed.
Cold winds chase the summer breeze,
The summer is going to bed.

Barry Blake (9)
Sandfield CP School

Flying Pig

One day, one strange day
Tuesday to be exact,
I saw a blue flying pig
And that's a definite fact.

I tried to tell my brother John
And also my dog Christen
I tried to tell the neighbourhood
But they just wouldn't listen.

I told everyone I knew
About what I had seen
But they just laughed and said
'What a fool she's been!'

So no one believed me
What should I do?
Maybe you'll believe me
If I told you.

Elizabeth Ellis (11)
Sandfield CP School

Favourite Food

Jelly beans, all sorts of things,
Chocolate bars and sweetie jars.
Treacle tarts and chocolate hearts,
Crispies and biscies plus Hula Hoops
With tomato soup.
Croutons and fruit bombs,
Those are my favourite foods.

Victoria Howlett (9)
Sandfield CP School

The Boy

The autistic boy, walking down the street
Saying 'Hello' but no one did speak.
One big world crammed into a little brain
Nervous and confused, all at once.
Stepping into a crammed, bright coloured shop,
Picking up a tube of some sort.
Slipping each shiny coin onto the desk
Staring at the man with a pair of green, shiny eyes.
Turning quickly and rushing out
Turning right at the roundabout and left at the lights.
Suddenly, a trip, a fall, a pain
The technicolour rocks rolling away,
Away, away, away.

Liberty Pollock (10)
Sandfield CP School

The King Of Spain

Poor King of Spain
He had a pain
In his brain
He's gone insane!

Doctor Jill said
'You're very ill
Here take a pill
Now go home and chill.'

He couldn't get a train
He was stuck in the rain
I'm feeling better
But much, much wetter.

Christina Drain (11)
Sandfield CP School

In The Classroom

Look into the classroom window,
You see, all is quiet.
But what you see in there after school
Can soon turn into a riot.

Down falls the blackboard
As it zooms into life,
Down falls the metre-sticks,
Before you could say 'Jack Knife!'

Down comes the washing line
That children use for PE
As a skipping rope
Dear me, dear me!

So if you're looking in a classroom window,
If there's something weirder that you see
Could you please write a letter
Or come and tell me?

Natalie Parsons (11)
Sandfield CP School

School

School is fun, school is great
Everyone there has a mate!

The lessons are fun and so is the play
I want to be there every day!

The teachers are nice and they're kind
I do miss my mum but never mind.

Annabel Holland (9)
Sandfield CP School

Sisters

Playing in the park
Is always so much fun
But when I go home
I've got to get my homework done.

Doing all my homework
Makes me feel quite sad
As whilst I'm trying to do it
My sisters make me mad.

My sisters are annoying,
They scream, they shout, they bawl,
I try to get things done
But they drive me up the wall.

Sometimes sisters are quite nice
It's not actually that bad
They keep me from getting lonely
Which makes me really glad.

Alejandra Young (10)
Sandfield CP School

Silly Billy

There once was a boy called Billy
Who was extremely silly
He did not know French
So he sat on the bench,
That dunce of a boy called Billy.

Louise Blake (9)
Sandfield CP School

School

Please we beg you!
Don't you feel sad
To send us to school
It really makes us mad.

You give us an apple
And off we go
To a terrible place
Friends nor foe.

And about maths
They give you a dice
And check your work
And say it's not nice.

And when it's play
A child starts to cry
But the teachers just turn round
And give no reply.

Katrien Loots (10)
Sandfield CP School

Winter

W onderful winter is white when it snows,
 I mprints of footsteps lie around down below
N ever again does it seem there'll be heat,
T errible it seems, there's no warmth on the street
E ven if it's beautiful, you want spring to come,
R eturning life with the radiance of the sun.

Carolyn Smith (10)
Sandfield CP School

A Job

I'm going to get a job,
I'll earn a lot of money
I'll come back very rich,
Just you wait and see.

I'll take with me a suitcase,
I'll pack everything I need,
The biggest bag of sweets ever,
And a comic book to read.

Perhaps I'll be a pirate,
And live on the seven seas,
Or maybe a jungle explorer,
I'd swing from tree to tree.

I really love the sun,
But I also love the snow.
The desert or Antarctica
I don't know where to go.

Fantastic, I've got it,
The perfect job for me.
I'll be the king in Buckingham Palace,
But first - I'll have my tea.

Lily Speer (11)
Sandfield CP School

Easter

Every Easter the bunny comes,
and brings us eggs and hot cross buns.

Daffodils hatch out from the Earth
Spring is here bringing birth.

Chicks and kittens, they're so cute,
I love Easter, don't you too?

Amy Dziwulski (10)
Sandfield CP School

All Things

Pickle and jam,
Custard and ham,
And would you drink a toad?

Would you eat a slug?
Or will you chew on a bug?
Or do you prefer to eat a mug?

Do you want a cup of tea?
Do you want to eat a pea?
Or would you just prefer a carrot?

Children play,
Horses eat hay,
But none of them have to pay.
Summer is great
If it's sitting on a plate,
But it's not very fun in winter.

Lewis Ellis (10)
Sandfield CP School

The World

Our world is round like a huge football
With many living things big and small
As years have gone by, there have been lots of changes,
Affecting different sceneries in different places.

There are many beautiful features
All around the world to be seen
With many lovely colours it's like a fantastic dream
I'm really telling you everything, you must've seen something.

Reece Killick (11)
Sandfield CP School

My Gerbils

My gerbils are extremely friendly
If you put your hand out
Their soft, small, furry bodies will rub against you.
Their little noses with long whiskers on
Will tickle your outstretched hand.

My gerbils are very nosy
And will chew anything (including their water bottle)
They are as black as charcoal right down to the tips of their long tails.
There is an occasional squeak, but otherwise all is quiet.

My gerbils' cage is like an underground maze,
When they're not sleeping or eating, they're digging a new tunnel
In their soft, papery sawdust.
Every morning I come downstairs to find a new world hidden
                                              in their cage.

Hannah Norman (11)
Sandfield CP School

Pig Poem

Pigs oh pigs rolling in muck
They get told off every day for chasing the farmer's pet duck.
'Hey, leave him alone, go chase a mouse,
If I have to pay one more vet bill
We'll be in the poor house.

That's it, to the sausage factory with you
Now get in the truck, come on Hue.
Come on now get in here
I will have you in a bun later this year.'

Christopher West (11)
Sandfield CP School

The Bogeyman

He's big and hairy
and extremely scary.

He has long spiky hair
And is as tall as a bear.

He tries to grab you in the night
But watch out, he's a terrible sight.

His hands come through the door
And he steps quietly on the floor.

He huffs and puffs trying to blow you away
So be careful otherwise you'll pay!

Yalda Keshavarzi (11)
Sandfield CP School

From The Meadow

The falling leaves look like a rainbow of snow,
The rustling of leaves sounds like a snake slithering through
the leaves.
The singing birds sound like children singing,
The children in the woods make squeaking sounds.
Like little mice having fun.
The puffy clouds are like lovely soft toys to cuddle.
The view of houses make a nice rainbow of different styles
of brown.
The aeroplane flew past and looked like a flash of lighting.

Eloise Perry (9)
Shottermill Junior School

From The Meadow

If you stop and look closely into the meadow,
You will see the proper beauty.

Aeroplanes fly overhead,
Like gigantic birds patrolling the autumn skies.

Tree trunks sit still in the autumn breeze,
Like huge fingers pointing towards the heavens.

The big white clouds are
Like the guardian monsters of Heaven's gates.

The cars are like different coloured giant beetles
Scuttling down concrete paths.

The brambles are like the spiky version
Of a jellyfish's tentacles.

The trees undress in autumn
One leaf strays
And flutters down to a glittering blue stream.

David Boxall (9)
Shottermill Junior School

From The Meadow

A bird like a phoenix with its mythical song.
A leaf is a star of heavenly greatness dancing in the air.
Water, many, many tears of the sea god, form the ocean.
And the golden sun with pure greatness.
Finally the crystal-coloured egg of rebirth.

Alexander Bass (9)
Shottermill Junior School

An Autumn Walk

As I walk along, dancing sunrays shine through the trees
All the different colours   red
                                   yellow
                                   brown
                                   gold and russet
Sapphire-blue sky and fluffy white clouds
Squirrels collect acorns
I gather sweet chestnuts and horse chestnuts
I step on the leaves, a crunching sound it makes,
                                   rustling,
A gush of wind
          whooshing
          whistling
          sighing and
          whispering
I skip home to bake my chestnuts.

Solomon Lawes (8)
Shottermill Junior School

From The Meadow

You could hear the birds,
Singing softly to the sound of nature.
The tree overhanging the blades of grass
In the meadow,
A house in the distance
Painted with a pure white coating
On the balcony overlooking the valley.

The breeze brushing the grass
Still swaying with the wet dew,
Drying in the light of the scorching sun
Shouting sounds in the distance
From children in the woods.

Nicholas Cherrill (9)
Shottermill Junior School

I Love Autumn

I love
Autumn mornings when the air is freezing,
Autumn mornings when the birds are calling,
Autumn mornings when there is a mighty breeze,
Autumn mornings when the apples are falling.

I love
Autumn afternoons when the sun is shining,
Autumn afternoons when the children are playing,
Autumn afternoons when the wind is blowing,
Autumn afternoons when the conkers are falling.

I love
Autumn evenings when the rain is falling,
Autumn evenings when sunset fills the sky,
Autumn evenings when fireworks are flashing,
Autumn evenings when we sit by the fire.

Edward Gibson (8)
Shottermill Junior School

Ronny Rees

Ronny Rees,
Ate chocolate cheese,
It made him feel quite sick.
Naomi Nees,
Ate stale peas,
She stirred them with a stick.

Ben Everitt (8)
Shottermill Junior School

The Wind

A lonely voice,
Calling out for love and warmth,
But taking with it
A coldness and unease
Spreading everywhere like a disease.

A child,
Lost in a crowd,
Crying for someone no one's seen,
But when help comes he sends it away,
To be alone for another day.

An old man,
Unmoving like a stopped clock,
Waiting to be wound
But no tear falls from his eye.
All he does is sigh.

A steel bar,
Hammering at your door,
Scraping the windows
Crushing all in its way,
It's going to make you pay.

A raging flood,
A single drop as weak as a newborn lamb,
A torrent as strong as a diamond,
Covering everything with its icy body,
Who can stop it? Nobody.

A forest fire,
Bringing dread when it's angry.
Destroying everything in its path,
Not caring about families or friends,
Just wanting their lives to end.

Cleo Stringer (10)
South Farnham Junior School

The School Trip

The school trip proved to be a manic day,
We went to a theme park without delay,
The driver drove over ninety miles an hour,
And acted like he had some super power!

He drove us around all over the road,
And showed his amazing blue pet toad,
He had a moustache that he'd dyed scarlet-red,
And to keep cool in summer he'd shaved his large head!

When we got to the theme park we jumped up and down,
And saw the best ride called 'Munjo the Clown'!
We rushed over to it and shouted, 'Whoopee!'
'We'll go on here first Miss, we smiled with glee.

Then we got on and sat with our friends,
The roller coaster went round some terrific bends,
Most of the boys were violently sick,
To distract them a teacher performed a great trick!

As we went home we sang silly songs,
Others held their noses and said, 'Eww it pongs!'
Somebody's drink, well, it started to drip,
I'm not sure I liked that strange school trip!

Holly Hunt (11)
South Farnham Junior School

William

On Sunday I ride William
He is a horse of course!
As I arrive in the morning my face still yawning
I get on my horse.
In rain or shine he is mine.
Sometimes William is slow then I have to use my crop
Sometimes he is fast and hard to stop.
When we are out on a ride he stops for a snack
And nearly throws me off his back.
With the wind in my hair it seems I don't care.

Helena Essex (10)
South Farnham Junior School

Something

Something is creaking the bedroom door
Something is moving across the floor
Something is whistling in the hall
Something is roaring a hopeful call
Something is howling very loud
Something is raging as though it is proud
Something is forcing the chair to rock
Something is whispering over the tick of the clock.

Something is deadly when in a swirl
Something is strong enough to push over a girl
Something is blowing into my ear
Something is bellowing but is too high to hear
Something is around me all the time
Something is making a beautiful rhyme
Something is happening, the light is dimmed
Something, this something is called the
                    'wind'

Amelia Leishman (11)
South Farnham Junior School

Once Upon A Rhyme

M is for Mum is always there to help
Y is for yummy cake half eaten on the table.

B is for birthday one whole year older
I is for icing on the cake
R is for rest after the party
T is for the time when everyone has to go
H is for happiness everybody's having fun
D is for dancing to the music
A is for all the candles on my cake
Y is for yippee, everyone is happy.

Polly Rattue (10)
South Farnham Junior School

Rain Is . . .

Rain is
a million teardrops falling from the sky.
Rain is
a thousand fingers tapping on the window.
Rain is
soldiers marching across the rooftops.
Rain is
a waterfall cascading over a rock face.
Rain is
trickling streams running down your face.
Rain is
a veil of mist across your eyes.
Rain is
a drink for a thirsty plant
Rain is
the bringer of life.
Rain is
sad,

grey,

drizzle.

Ben Smith (10)
South Farnham Junior School

Red Roses

Rosy red roses all in a line,
Sweet smell of perfume wafting around velvet, red petals,
Swaying in the wind oh so elegant and slim,
Rosy red roses all in a line,
Some red as blood some nearly pink,
Long-stemmed roses very romantic
No flower bed is complete without rosy red roses
Arches of roses around the door
Bouquets of roses on a wedding day
Red petals scattered on the path look beautiful for a bride to pass,
Rosy red roses all in a line
Pollen for bees, nectar for butterflies,
Spiky green stems prick your fingers,
Rosy red roses all in a line,
Some roses in bushes some on the wall,
Some climbing roses scramble through trees,
Pretty on our bowls and plates,
Vases of roses on the table,
Inspire artists to capture their beauty,
Rosy red roses all in a line.

Jennifer Keel (10)
South Farnham Junior School

My Motorbike

Blue as the sky
Fast as the wind
My dream come true
A Yamaha Mark Two.

Number twenty-four
Coming through
Determined to be placed
But I am still very new.

It's getting very muddy and wet
Slipping all over it's raining too
Perhaps I must just scrape through.

My heart's in my mouth
I'm almost there
The finish line is just over there.

Give her a rev and hold on tight
I'm gonna win this race
With all my might.

Going up and down hills
Getting closer every time
Soon that trophy will be mine.

These thoughts keep me going when I'm tired
Winning the race will get me hired
Here I come down the straight
Hoping that I'm not too late.

I crossed the line
I've won the race
My dream's come true
Me and my Yamaha so blue.

Jack Miller (11)
South Farnham Junior School

The King

'O King,' said the people
As he wandered through the town,
Footing it through the streets
Wearing a regal gown
He walked through the streets
Whilst staring at the sky,
There's no doubt about it,
He's a very popular guy!

The king was very stupid,
Though few knew and no one admitted it,
His crown was on at a strange angle,
But he loved the crown maker who fitted it.
His nose was large and his ears too,
And his mouth was somewhat small,
His neck seemed joined to his head,
And he looked like he'd had a bad fall.

The king was a sensitive fellow,
He didn't like being insulted,
If his subjects didn't pretend they adored him,
He'd eat their ears roasted and salted.
The king took over the government
He scrapped the prime minister position,
With only a little help from
The king's scheming private tactician.

This king never saw a psychiatrist,
They thought him a danger to the country.
He got his revenge by paying them little,
Or literally paying them poultry.
He tried to bring back executions,
This isn't a popular thing,
There's definitely no denying it . . .
Charles wasn't a very good king!

Jake Duthie (11)
South Farnham Junior School

Football Players

F igo, fast and furious,
   keeps the midfield alive.
O wen, striker sensation,
   scores goals for us to win.
O akes, killer keeper,
   wolf-like he defends his cave.
T hierry Henry, upfront hero,
   hits hard at the net.
B eckham, wing wizard,
   creates footie fireworks from free kicks.
A shley Cole, defending demon,
   burns like hot coal.
L ouis Saha, streaking striker,
   streamlines the shots superbly.
L ampard, lion-hearted and lucky,
   loves to leave the opposition lacking.

      But my team would not be winners-to-be
      Without the skill and dedication of a
      Player like me!

George Carroll (10)
South Farnham Junior School

My Story

I was born on the twenty-fifth of June,
I play a few instruments that make a cool tune.
I broke my leg when I was only two,
Now I like to run around, write diaries and other things too.

So this is my life story, come and join in,
It's not that boring, so don't throw it in the bin.

Singing is my hobby, rock music and pop too.
Maybe one day I will release a number one single wahoo!
I go to school most days, except when I'm ill and weekends,
Which I then spend having fun trying to keep up with the trends.

So this is my life story, come and join in,
It's not that boring, so don't throw it in the bin.

My sister is called Megan,
She's thirteen and I'm eleven.
I have two brothers Lucian and Sebastian,
I give them a cuddle whenever I can.

So this is my life story, come and join in,
It's not that boring, so don't throw it in the bin.

I have a mum, who's really great,
She is a lawyer, and must never be late.
I have a dad who plays the guitar,
He's in a band and is a *Rock star*.

So this is my life story, come and join in,
It's not that boring, so don't throw it in the bin.

I also have a stepmum, her name is Lynne,
When it comes to her cooking, it never goes in the bin.
As well as that, I have a stepdad, his name is Silviu,
He comes from the country Romania, and his name is pronounced
Silvio.

So this is my life story, it has now come to an end
You know most things about me, now just read it to a friend.

Alexandra Johnstone (10)
South Farnham Junior School

Midnight Eyes

Cat's eyes in the middle of the night,
Glaring, staring eyes of light,
Midnight eyes.

Tiger's eyes in the middle of the night,
Electric yellow and extremely bright,
Midnight eyes.

Fox's eyes in the middle of the night,
Red and round from such vile fights,
Midnight eyes.

Wolf's eyes in the middle of the night,
Facing the moon and howling with all might,
Midnight eyes.

Lion's eyes in the middle of the night,
Yawning loudly pupils squashed tight,
Midnight eyes.

Dog's eyes in the middle of the night,
Carefully watching left and right,
Midnight eyes.

Cheetah's eyes in the middle of the night,
Stalking prey from treetops high,
Midnight eyes.

Crocodile's eyes in the middle of the night,
Watching quietly waiting for a bite,
Midnight eyes.

Rhino's eyes in the middle of the night,
Charging angrily because of poor eyesight,
Midnight eyes.

Owl's eyes in the middle of the night,
Looking through my window and giving me a fright,
Midnight eyes . . .

Christy Humphreyies (11)
South Farnham Junior School

The Animal Alphabet

A is for all the animals
B is the bats that screech out loud
C is for cats crawling around
D is for dolphins which splash around
E is for the giant elephant
F is for fish which blow small bubbles
G is for the giraffe with its JCB neck,
H is for the tall neighing horse
I is for the intelligent iguana
J is for the jaguar as black as night
K is for the kitten so fluffy and bright
L is for the woolly lamb,
M is for a monkey hanging on a tree
N is for the horned nanny goat
O is for the big feathered ostrich
P is for the smelly fat pig
Q is for the queen bee busy in her hive
R is for the long-tailed rat
S is for the long snake
T is for the stripy tiger,
U is for the ugly duckling
V is for the small sweet vole
W is for the enormous gentle whale
X is for the love birds in love
Y is for the yellow canary singing in his cage
Z is for the forest asleep after dark.

Ruby Rowell (10)
South Farnham Junior School

At Midnight . . .

At midnight the ghosts come out,
Zombies moan and mad doctors shout.

Vampire suck on people's necks,
Pirate ghosts fall dead on their decks,
The overgrown baby starts to eat,
Then there's always the wailing white sheet!

At midnight the ghosts come out,
Zombies moan and mad doctors shout,

The dark prince swings his baseball bat,
You don't want to meet the human cat,
And although he just fell through the floor,
The rotten smelling zombie is back for more!

At midnight the ghosts come out,
Zombies moan and mad doctors shout.

Frankenstein has invaded my room,
The aliens spell certain doom,
And the monster who lives under my bed,
Is poking out his ugly head!

At midnight the ghosts come out,
Zombies moan and mad doctors shout.

Spiders come from round the clock,
Ghost ships begin to dock,
Alien spaceships come out of the sky,
Surely the werewolf means I will die!

At midnight the ghosts come out,
Zombies moan and mad doctors shout,

The ghost train is coming near,
The witch is filling me with fear,
The Egyptian mummy is at my rear,
Someone get me out of here!

Robin Humphreyies (11)
South Farnham Junior School

The Rainforest

Birds of every colour,
Flashing in the trees,
All the toucans are singing
Sweet, sweet melodies.

The chimps are swinging
Through the trees
The sun is bursting
Through the leaves.

Shades of green
Shades of brown
Up to the treetops
And the monkeys
Climb down.

Poison arrow frogs
Leaping in the haze
Teams of ants
Crawling through
The wriggly root maze.

Slithering tree serpents
Swaying in the branches
The strong slow sloth
Slowly munches.

Gliding geckos
Soaring gently
Amongst the trees
A jaguar prowling
Stalking everything
That he sees.

The Cock of the Rock
Standing high to attention
As he does his daily wrenching,
As the day is slowly ending.

Rufus Driscoll (11)
South Farnham Junior School

Siege Of Gondor

A radiant beauty,
A beacon of light,
The city of Osgiliath,
Under the sun so bright.

The darkness was rising,
Over the trees and hills,
Minus-Morgal emptied,
Marching for wars thrills.

Came a leader so frightening,
Terrible and bold,
Riding an evil creature,
With a heart stone cold.

Then came the battle,
With a terrible roar,
Spilled everywhere,
Was blood and gore.

The stakes were high,
The battle was fierce,
But in the end,
The walls were pierced.

The men of Osgiliath,
Lay sprawled on the floor,
They had been defeated,
By Minus-Morgal.

George Keenan (11)
South Farnham Junior School

Our New Baby

Our family's expanding, our new baby's on its way
Is it a boy or a girl? We'll know any day.
My brother or sister will be my new friend
Now we've got to think of another new name.
Who'll look after me whilst Mum's in pain?
Will it be born in the sunshine, the light of the day
Or in the quiet dark night with the stars shining bright?
I'm happy, excited, I just can't wait,
All the not knowing I really do hate.
Up goes the cot, pram down from the loft,
We've bought it a teddy all cuddly and soft.
Mum's very tired she needs lots of rest
She asks us to help her and we all do our best.
I'm the proud big brother, I'll help all I can
After all, all too soon I'll be a grown-up man.
Pink or blue clothes, we've got them all ready
When it learns to sit, crawl and stand, I'll be here to help steady.
What will it look like, blonde, bald or fat,
Hungry and crying or asleep like the cat?
Dribbly chin, smelly nappies, and long sleepless nights
My sister's just two, I remember it all.
Breastfeeds and cuddles and supporting her neck,
Quiet and gentle, no loud music - oh heck!
Lying flat on its back, feet to the bottom of the cot,
Room temperature right, it mustn't be too hot.
A brand new beginning, a new special life,
We'll love it forever, for that we will strive.

Matthew Parrott (10)
South Farnham Junior School

The Lake Of Fury Free

I shall set off and go now,
And go to where peace runs freely,
The Lake of Fury Free.
And a small hut I'll build there,
Made of stone and soft, soft clay.
I'll make a little bird's house,
For the perfect hummingbirds.

I will set off and go now,
To the Lake of Fury Free.
There'll be a hive for the honeybee,
And a forest of bluebells for the butterfly.

I must set off and go now,
To the Lake of Fury Free.
The beavers, busy building
The butterflies flapping and flittering
The hummingbird singing and humming
The kingfisher fishing and floating,
The honeybee is buzzing,
By the Lake of Fury Free.

Free of bombers,
Free of guns,
And free of mines.
Free of greed,
Free of anger,
And free of envy.
Free of hate,
Free of people,
I shall set off and go now,
To the Lake of Fury Free.

Kathryn Burke   (10)
South Farnham Junior School

Mystery Field

The redcoats marched to battle in Mystery Field,
As the guns and their teams trundled down the road,
The cavalry rode beside,
All those people, horses and all,
Destined to die in Mystery Field.

The skirmishes fought in Mystery Field,
The riflemen, voltigeurs and Light Companies,
Were first on the battlefield,
As they poured shot and bullet into each other's sides,
As the infantry arrived on Mystery Field.

The redcoats fired their volleys in Mystery Field,
As the guns fired in a ceaseless rhythm,
Shouted orders and repeated commands,
Inaudible above the chaos of noise,
Horses snorting, sergeants cursing, bullets humming in the air,
The redcoats advance, the enemy break,
The cavalry race after the running soldiers,
The redcoats have victory on Mystery Field.

Death had visited Mystery Field,
Thousands upon thousands had died,
Just as many wounded or close to death,
Every victory has a price, as with defeat,
This was the price they had to pay,
This is what happened on Mystery Field.

Jack Deare (10)
South Farnham Junior School

Jack Frost

The sky was a spill of magical ink,
The snow fell down like stars,
And Jack Frost crept out on the lonely street,
No shops, no kids, no cars.

An icy blast filled the air,
An earthquake hit the ground,
Swirling, soft, sensational snowflakes,
Danced gracefully all around.

A sack was slung over his shoulder,
His eyes were like balls of snow,
He watched as the moon lay before him,
Wondering which way to go.

Clambering carefully up the side of a house,
He looked inside his sack,
Then carried on going higher and higher,
No sign of turning back.

The wind was a wolf howling quite loud,
When Jack Frost was done for the night,
If there's ice on your window in the morning
And you guess it's Jack Frost, you are right.

Helen Schnabel (11)
South Farnham Junior School

A Spring Morning

I love this Canadian spring morning,
With its fresh, cool air,
As bouncing clouds float by,
The snow-capped mountains stand up high.

As blue, pure water trickles down,
From towering mountains to the ground,
It forms a meander, twirling and swirling,
For the ice-cold water won't be returning.

By the lake, purple wild berries grow,
And highly scented flowers spring from below
Attracting chocolate-coloured bears,
Emerging from forests to and fro.

Mother bears, rabbits and deer,
Lead their children to conquer their fears.
To drink by the lake, eat wild plants too,
Think of Mother Nature and all she's done for you.

Anneka Butters (10)
South Farnham Junior School

The Wild Stallion

He stands there looking out at the mountains.
As far as he can see is his kingdom.
His eyes are like pits of darkness
that go on forever.
They see all and miss nothing.
His nostrils flare as he senses danger in the distance.
In the wind, his mane flows like flaming fire on his neck.
His chestnut body upright and splendid.
Knows he must challenge the new intruder.
His strong legs thunder over the ground as he gallops
over the moorland.
In next to no time, the challenge is over.
He rears, he bucks, he is the winner.
He is the king,
He is 'The Wild Stallion'.

Charlotte Spratt (10)
South Farnham Junior School

My Search For Life On Mars

I'm closing in on the red planet
It looks wonderful from my hi-tec pod
I'm about to land and my heart is racing
I'm very excited and a little scared.

I've just landed at my destination
I can't wait to get out and explore
The pod door opens and the planet invites me out
I step slowly out onto the rocky ground.

I see cliffs all around me and as far as I can see
I hope I don't fall from one of the cliffs
I will go and start my search
and hope to find proof of life on Mars.

I've found water and ice so that could mean life
I must find samples to take back to Earth
Humans may be able to live on Mars too
That would be great to help our overcrowded planet.

Oh my word I can't believe it
I see someone - there is life on Mars
He is inviting me to see his family (I think)
Should I go? If I don't I will miss out.

I have found life on Mars but will it be friendly?

Sam Hughes (11)
South Farnham Junior School

Riding

Giddy, giddy, giddy, up, up, up,
My little pony.
We need to get going!
Up and up over the hill,
Canter then trot and maybe a gallop or two!

Giddy, giddy, giddy, up, up, up,
My little pony.
We need to get going!
Reins are short,
Stirrups long,
Girth tight
And off we go, for hack up the Wright's field!

Giddy, giddy, giddy, up, up, up,
My little pony,
We need to get going!

Jake Wright (10)
South Farnham Junior School

Underwater World!

Underwater world is wonderful,
The brightly coloured coral is beautiful,
It seems alive, sways from side to side,
Waving anemones in which creatures hide.

The fish dart around abruptly,
Stingrays glide magnificently,
Kelp forms a forest on the seabed,
A shipwreck conceals its gruesome dead.

The whales moan, the dolphins peep,
Their sound echoes into the deep.
Sharks and stingray, eat their meals,
To the sound of slithering eels.

The water's movement goes astray
Even when it gets its way!
It turns, it crawls, it sways, it makes a splash,
Waves come down with a crash.

The colours of the sea,
Are as dazzling as the sun to me,
All bright and cheery,
They'll never be dull and bleary.

Now as you can see, the sea is perfect for me!

Hannah Swannie (11)
South Farnham Junior School

Dreaming

Sitting in a field, dreams fill my mind of places I have never seen.
Places of happiness, places of fun, places of wisdom,
places to come.
Sitting dreaming, sitting dreaming, wishing and
wishing will it be me someday - in the sun?

Answer me, call me, I want to know some day.
I'm getting pictures, pictures of my holiday!
People riding the waves, swimming having fun.
Look there! Dolphins jumping in the blue sea
glistening in the sun.
Water sports are going on. People sipping colourful
drinks, watching all the surfers surfing.
People buying wonderful gifts for their family and
friends, shop assistants serving.

Ice cream vans serving happy people with cool
ice creams on the yellow sand.
Dogs splashing in the rock pools, children running
after them and then playing on the sand.
Kites gliding in the sky; yellow, red, blue, all the
colours I can dream of.

This dream of happiness, this dream of fun.
This dream of places to come.
Sitting dreaming, sitting dreaming, wishing and
wishing, will it be me some day.

Melissa Poole (11)
South Farnham Junior School

My Pets

I have two animals and seventeen fish,
one is a rabbit, and she eats from a dish.
Her name is Millie and she's brown and white,
and sometimes she and my guinea pig fight.

She lives in a hutch at the back of the house,
and sometimes shares it with a country mouse.
She loves her carrots and gnaws on bark,
and we cover her up when the sky gets dark.

On a nice day she goes out in her run,
and she loves to stretch in the afternoon sun.
We bought her a lead so she can run around,
and she hops across the garden without a sound.

We named our guinea pig Charlie Boy,
and he and my rabbit are full of joy.
He's champagne coloured and smooth to touch,
and he also lives with Millie in their big green hutch.

On cold damp evenings we bring them inside,
and Charlie likes to run and hide.
But Millie likes to watch TV,
and then she falls asleep on me.

My seventeen goldfish live in a pond,
and we have a wild bullfrog mum named Bond!
We feed them in the summer and they swim around a lot,
but we only see them when the weather gets hot!

Buried in the garden by the front door,
lie three other pets that are no more.
Benji, Fudge and Kali too,
we will remember them, our friends will too.

Amy Dawson (11)
South Farnham Junior School

The Beach In Tobago

I loved the beach in Tobago
Did ya hear me, I loved it!
The waves were higher than the trees
The lovely sand stuck to my skin
The Caribbean sun beating down on the beach
As hot as the Earth's core.
People laughing and shouting having lots of fun
Playing with bodyboards and lilos.
I can't believe it, I'm going on a speedboat
Riding the waves like a surfboard
Jumping so high, you have to hold on
Seeing so many beaches along the coast.

I loved the beach in Tobago
Did ya hear me, I loved it!
Listening to Reggae music on the sand
It was Bob Marley, it was sure to be grand
Guys with dreadlocks playing on the beach
Playing calypso to the sound of the beat
Men wearing Rasta hats playing the steel band
Sounding like seashells, bells, pots and pans.

Freddie Wilson (10)
South Farnham Junior School

About A Dog . . .

My dog Bramble likes to play
with her toys all day.
She is black and white, also brown.
Her eyebrows are big which gives her a frown.

She likes to play in puddles
which makes her fur all muddled.
She rolls in mud from head to tail
So we have to give her a bath.

She likes to chase squirrels and birds
but they get scared away fast.
Bramble likes to play fetch
with tennis balls or sticks.

When it snows she runs around
licking up all the snow off the ground.
When it's all sunny she likes to lie
in all the warm patches.

She goes to kennels when we go away
she makes dog friends and starts to play.
When she goes into her basket
Bramble sleeps and starts snoring.

Gareth Garland (11)
South Farnham Junior School

George

Open heath in front of me.
For miles and miles I can feel
All around me dew-covered grass.
The horizon's misty, the sky's like glass.

Pulling at my lead
I want to be let free
To run, to bound, to leap
Into the freedom of the day.

The sun is glistening on the droplets
Of rain on the heather.
I want to run, with my feet skimming the ground,
Not by my owner's side, with the constraint of a lead.

My owner's stopping,
She's stooping.
I hear the branches waving
Blown by a breeze.

There's a sudden movement of wind,
Her scarf is blown off;
She rushes to pick it up
With me at her side.

She folds it neatly, very carefully and slowly,
And places it delicately in her bag.
Then with a sigh she bends over me again,
I can smell her hand.

She's about to let me off, when she sees another dog
At the side of the heath,
She thinks I'll rush over,
So she doesn't let me go.

She waits till it's passed.
She's so uptight
When she gives me a glance.

I wait
For the sound of her clearing her throat,
Like chalk snapping,
A new crisp white.

Her shadow's darkly over me,
Hands glance my chin,
She twists my collar round
And grasps my lead.

She fiddles with my collar,
Fingers touch the clasp,
Her thumb pulls down the clip,
And then I hear, at last, at last, a satisfying click.

My owner lets go of my collar
And I'm off!
I run round a tree seven times
At the joy of my own pace.
The roar of sound in my ears
As the wind and I race,
The earth kicked up at my heels
And joy on my face.

All the wonderful smells around me,
The ditches, mud and rain,
And the scent of spring's plants
Make me excited again.

In the wind and the sun
I leap
I dance
And I let out a happy bark of laughter.

Harriet Foxwell (11)
South Farnham Junior School

My Mum

My mum is great!
She always changed my nappy,
Even when she wasn't happy,
She did all her chores,
And amazingly she didn't look bored!
My mum is great.

My mum is perfect!
She tucks me in at night,
Even saves me from a fright,
She taught me to draw,
And didn't complain about my dad, who does snore!
My mum is perfect!

My mum is amazing!
She does all the shopping,
Even all the mopping,
She even has time,
To drop her friend a line!
My mum is amazing!

Emily Corrigan (10)
South Farnham Junior School

We're Going To The Beach

Jump in the car,
It's not far
We're going to the beach,
Towels, cossies, it's in our reach,
We're going to the beach.

We're going to the beach,
Suncream, brolly, hats,
Don't forget the cricket bats.
We're going to the beach.

Mum stressed
Dad pressed
Brother and sister fighting
Baby crying
We're going to the beach.

Traffic jam,
Down roads we cram,
Car breaks down,
In the middle of town,
Hours waiting, waiting,
We're going to the beach.

Hooray, hooray, we're finally there
Storm breaks through, oh no!
Raining, raining, we're all soaked through,
At the beach.

Grace Molan (10)
South Farnham Junior School

Junk Food

Ice cream melts in your mouth,
It is eaten in the north, west, east and south.
Vanilla, strawberry and chocolate too
The flavour you choose is up to you!

Chocolate is a famous food
Which everyone loves to eat
It's very hard to resist
And is a special treat.

Crisps come in all shapes and sizes
Most of them are stuffed with prizes
I find them in my packed lunch
Eat them all day - including brunch!

Chips may be full of fat
But everyone loves them, fancy that!
Eat them with fish, eat them with ketchup
Put them in a sandwich and get indigestion!

Daniel Taylor (10)
South Farnham Junior School

The Snow

Hush, can you see the white blanket of snow,
How it's as white as an igloo that glows in the night?

Hush, can you smell the fresh snow in the cold air?

Hush, can you hear the crunching under your wellies
And the sliding of your feet?

Hush, can you taste the fresh water dingling and dangling
in your own mouth?

Hush, can you feel the hard freezing ice in your frozen hands
and fingers that turn into water that's nice and fresh?

Maneesha Maini (8)
West Dene School

Magic Lemonade

I wish I had magic lemonade
So it sparkles in my tummy,
It's yellow and it's really fizzy,
It makes my mouth feel funny.

I wish I had magic lemonade
It scorches and it blasts,
It makes me fiddle and wriggle,
It makes me laugh and laugh.

I wish I had magic lemonade
I love you, you're so bright,
You make my tastebuds tingle,
You are a fizzy drink delight!

Sona-Kineri Shah (7)
West Dene School

Moon

Moon you are as round as a ball,
You shine on us all.
Moon you are so bright
At night you make the light.
Moon, moon you are so high
You sing a lullaby in the sky.

Aku-Sheka Allotey (8)
West Dene School

Hush

Hush, can you see?

All the dancing flakes,
fluttering down to the blanket of white.

Hush, can you smell?

The icy cold freshness
of the snow,
that polishes the air.

Hush, can you hear?

All the shouting and crunching from
the mouths and boots
of excited children.

Hush, can you taste?

The dampness of the air,
tilt heads back and
taste the cold water.

Hush, can you feel?

The coldness wrapped
around your body like a blanket
until you go home and it'll leave.

Amanda Roper (8)
West Dene School

Rockets

Ten, nine, eight, seven, six, five, four, three, two, one
            Blast-off!
Rockets are smart, rockets are smooth,
Rockets go whizz, rockets go boom in the light
of the moon.

The stars round my rockets
Your eyes just drop
My rocket goes whizz, bang, pop.

Jackson Rhoden (7)
West Dene School

Hush Snow And Ice

Hush, can you see the snowball come, you are beautiful like cotton wool from Heaven, soft like a baby's bottom.

Hush, can you smell the cold air dream and as hard as ice is the stream if it breaks it feels like glass.

Hush, can you hear the birds give a tweet?
They are looking for something to eat.

Hush, can you taste the water? It's cold.
'Brrrr!' As cold as a polar bear and reindeer near to Santa Claus.

Hush, can you feel snow like water?
Please don't go you're beautiful.
I love you, so please don't melt, please!

Ayanna Blair-Ford (7)
West Dene School

Hush

Hush can you see the white coat of snow falling from the sky?
Look quickly before it melts.

Hush can you smell the fresh snow and the cold breeze?

Hush can you hear the 'crick' and 'crack' from down below your feet?

Hush can you taste the water dropping from your mouth?

Hush can you feel the cold in your hand and the soft snow?

Sydney Davy (7)
West Dene School

Hush

Hush can you see the blanket of thin white snow
and the cold breeze of gentle air?

Hush can you smell the crisp new air as it snows
and as you breathe the cold air?

Hush can you hear the cold breeze of air floating
through the sky as the clouds float by with it?

Hush can you taste the cold water in your mouth?

Hush can you feel the ice-cold snow in your hands
as it melts?

Sebastian Adeniran-Olule (8)
West Dene School

Star

Star that glitters through the night,
Star that glitters ever so bright.
You grant wishes before night
Lovely star of light.
But soon you'll be gone from the sky,
Please don't go or I will cry.
You light the way every night,
Lovely star of light.
There are many stars in the sky,
But you are the best, I don't know why.

Alice Kerbeck (8)
West Dene School